DICE OF THE GODS

The vignette is reproduced from a tetradrachm issued
in Catana (Sicily) between 461 and 455 B.C. It
probably represents the random creation of life on
earth taught by Empedocles. Viable creatures such
as waterfowl and fish are included as well as non-
viable ones such as the man-faced bull.

DICE OF THE GODS

Causality, Necessity and Chance

by

W. Ehrenberg, D.Sc.

Professor Emeritus of Experimental Physics
in the University of London

Copies are available through

Physics Department,
Birkbeck College,
University of London,
Malet Street,
London WC1E 7HX

Printed by G.G. Stevenson (Printers) Ltd., Dundee, Scotland

Preface

The world was credited with strict causality; science was believed to be based on nature obeying all-pervasive laws. But in the last few decades we have been alerted to the impossibility of carrying through a fully deterministic scheme.

In an attempt to elucidate this situation, I have brought together the wisdom of the philosophers and the expertise of modern physicists; an analysis of the concepts of causality, necessity and chance should reveal their role in the interpretation of nature. The quest necessarily extends to the history of these ideas, in order to learn its dated, but not out-dated lessons, - and to the foundation of modern physics. I hope the text will be found both accurate and lucid.

The burden of these studies is, briefly, to show up the difference between the ideas of cause and necessity, and to demonstrate and to explain how consciousness of chance, alive in antiquity, then almost suppressed for centuries, returned first as an insight into the human situation and a few decades later as a discovery in physics. Chance, causality and necessity are features of the world we live in and which we explore.

London 1975   W.E.

Werner Ehrenberg died in November 1975. In this book, which represents the work of his last years, he combined two of his main interests, classical philosophy and science. At the time of his death the manuscript was complete in draft form, although he would undoubtedly have revised the text and included more complete references. In the present edition the original manuscript remains substantially unaltered. Some minor corrections have been made and a number of references added and I am greatly indebted to Dr. J. C.E. Jennings for help with this task. Although the author was denied the opportunity of putting the final touches to his work, it is my hope that the book will nevertheless prove to be a fitting memorial to Werner Ehrenberg.

London 1977   M.E.

Contents

Introduction

Ideas of cause and effect have been with us since pre-historic times and have been the subject of much thought in the last few decades. Referring in particular to this topic, Léon Brunschvicg reminded us fifty years ago that the study of one's predecessors' work was essential even for a genius if he was to avoid, as a scientist, merely rediscovering known facts or, as a philospher, merely repeating fallacious arguments long since corrected. Some authors have responded to the challenge of modern discoveries in physics to established ideas of causality, and have disregarded Brunschvicg's warning with, I believe, exactly the consequences foreseen. I have here attempted to take up the discussion by bringing together the ancient wisdom of the philosophers and the expertise of modern physicists. My essay is therefore based both on a review of the history of the ideas of cause and chance and a description of the relevant developments in physics.

Cause, chance and necessity are factors in human activities as well as in philosophy and the sciences. I am concerned mainly with those aspects which are relevant in the area where philosophy and science meet. It will be shown how awareness of chance, alive in antiquity, then almost suppressed for centuries, returned first as an insight, into the human situation and a few decades later as a discovery in physics into which it was eventually - though not without reluctance, - systematically incorporated.

The terms basic in this essay have not always been endowed with an unambiguous meaning nor are they so endowed now. They may therefore require some introduction. Only 'causality' and its derivatives seem to have held a relatively stable meaning. Examples of causality in its narrower, and I believe proper, sense are not hard to find: thus we speak of infection as the cause of a fever. A cause always has reference to a particular aspect of a situation; it is concerned with a break in the continuous flow of events. Aristotle distinguished several types of cause, some of which are now considered as irrelevant or fictitious. But the question remained whether all events had causes and to what extent they determined their effect.

If we refer to a situation as unconditionally given by another, normally preceding situation, we speak of necessity. An obvious example is the relation of death to life. In a stricter sense necessity means that the later situation is completely and always given by the preceding one. The scheme of Euclidean geometry is often quoted as an analogue. The real test of the rule of necessity must be based on the study of atoms and elementary particles, i.e. on situations where the number of contributing parameters is small. The theory that necessity controls everything is called determinism.

If, however, necessity is not confirmed, and events occur for which we find no causes, we may conclude that what happens there, happens by chance. Do the gods gamble? Can we at all think in terms of chance? Do things really happen by themselves, or do we simply confess ignorance if we talk of chance?

Finally, a word about fate: Fate relates significant events in the life of men or communities to influences which are beyond their control, and beyond scientific understanding. The notion of fate is historically important, and still recognised by millions of people.

An now, reader, read on.

1
Fate, Cause and Necessity

The concept of a nature in which things happen developed slowly. Early, or primitive man, interpreted natural events as part of his communal life. Primitive man had no idea of impersonal forces; for him nature acted by social norms, which could be violated only at risk of retribution.

Regular occurrences remain unnoticed in the background; primitive man does not ask why they happened; he is alerted only if the event is a misfortune, or otherwise emotionally privileged, and then he traces it to an evil spell, or interprets the event as retribution for an evil deed done by a member of his tribe, or for an act of homage neglected. The cause produces the effect, in the way a craftsman manufactures his spearhead. Just as today, evil influences were normally believed to have come from other tribes. Kelsen (1943) reports that the Bakauris in central Brazil have one and the same word for 'we', 'our' and 'good' and another for 'not we', 'bad', 'unhealthy'. Diseases are not taken as merely physical ailments: the medicine man must find the offence committed which caused them - and the offence is a substance that must be removed by an act of purification such as the ceremonial of mysteries or a public confession.

Primitive man does not think in terms of chance. On the other hand, he knows no interwoven network of causes, he sees only separate strands which have a beginning - say the violation of the magician's susceptibilities - and an end, - perhaps a tribesman's sudden death; he does not worry about what happens in the interval. He makes no attempt to establish contiguity in a cause-effect relation, and hence he has no means of checking a particular cause-effect relation; he accepts the first inspiration about the cause he conceives, and would not be prepared to take the risk of not responding to his inspiration. If he attributes a man's death to another man's witchcraft, it would not occur to him to enquire in what way this witchcraft acted, or what physiological changes produced the death.

These notions are reflected in classical Greek mythology. In particular, the forecasts of the oracles lack contiguity. Certain events had the privilege of being forecast, for a moderate fee; normally the stages leading to the events, however, were left undetermined. It was like a game of chess with an unquestionably superior partner, where you know you will lose, but you don't know how. Whatever steps King Laius took, *fate* would cause him to be killed by his son Oedipus, Iocaste's child. The idea of fate as a discontinuous causality is not extinct: during the last war it was frequently heard that a bomb would not find you unless it 'had your name on it'. Such stories and explanations are a genuine element of humanity's dialogue with nature through which man makes himself familiar with the world into which he is dropped. Freud, if no one else, has reminded us of the eternal truth these ideas contain. But we are not readily reconciled to the absence of contiguity.

Circumstances have forced people to accept the idea of forces acting at a distance against their inclination, as happened after the initial rejection of Newton's discovery of gravitation - but then acceptance was the recognition of a fact rather than an explanation. We require a temporally and spatially unbroken sequence of intermediate links. Such a sequence of links does not exist between the priest who every morning walks up the hill before sunrise and lights a candle, and the reappearance of the sun; or between the witchdoctor who sticks a needle into the wax figure of a person, and the victim's death. But links are found between the presence of impurities in a semi-conductor and its conductivity, or between the presence of anopheles mosquitoes and the occurrence of malaria.

The first explicit discussion of the problems of causality is given in *Plato's Phaedo (429-347)*. In this dialogue Socrates, facing execution (399 B.C.), was asked by his friends why he did not try to escape. Replying, Socrates reminisces:

...'I lost no time in procuring the books of Anaxagoras ... as I read on I discovered that the fellow made no use of mind and assigned to it no causality for the order of the world, but deduced causes like air and ether and water and many other absurdities. It seemed to me that he was just about as inconsistent as if someone were to say 'the cause of everything that Socrates does is mind' and then ... said that the reason why I am here now is that my body is composed of bones and sinews ... and this is the cause of my sitting here in bent position ...., and never troubled to mention the real reasons, which are, since Athens has thought better to condemn me, therefore I for my part have thought it better to sit here, and more right to stay and submit to whatever penalty she orders - because I fancy that these sinews and bones would have been in the neighbourhood of Megara or Boetia long ago if I did not think that it was more right and honourable to submit to whatever penalty my country orders rather than take to my heels and run away. If it were said that without such bones and sinews and all the rest of them I should not be able to do what I think is right, it would be true; but to say that it is because of them that I do what I am doing, and not through choice of what is best - although my actions are controlled by mind - would be a very lax and inaccurate form of expression. Fancy being unable to distinguish between the cause of a thing, and the condition without which it could not be a cause!'

This beautiful and moving passage has here a three-fold significance. First, it has outgrown all mythology and magic. Secondly, it indicates a logical classification of causes: the bodily movements appear as proximate causes, that is as a cause immediately affecting the location of the body, whereas the mind, controlling the movements of the bones, is the remote and, according to Socrates, the truly relevant cause. Finally, it is worth noting that the cause appears as answer to a specific question, viz. the reason why Socrates is in prison awaiting execution. We may of course be left to wonder how the mind can control the movement of the bones, a problem much discussed in the following millenia.

Aristotle

Aristotle (384-322) was the founder of the doctrines of cause and effect and of chance. Almost everything that has been written since about cause and chance is either directly or indirectly based on his ideas.

Aristotle takes over from earlier thinkers the division of the world into a heavenly and a sub-lunar sphere. The former is, apart from circular motion, unchanging and eternal. The sub-lunar world, i.e. the earth, is a world of becoming, of growth and decay. And it is this becoming which, as Aristotle saw it, is subject to the rules of cause and effect. Physics is concerned with understanding how this sub-lunar world of change works, how and why living things are generated and decay and artefacts are made, how objects change places, how events come about. What Aristotle calls physics comprises all sciences with the exception of astronomy. We have understood this world when we have found the causes of change.

Aristotle discerns four kinds of causes, without claiming that these are the only kinds, or that they necessarily apply to all objects, or are always clearly distinguishable. They reflect ways of looking at a situation, or ways of asking questions or of planning to act.

Any concrete object first of all consists of a material - a statue consists of marble - and this will be its *material cause.* Matter, essentially formless, is mere possibility, potentiality *(dynamis).* In our world, matter has also a form, e.g. the marble has the form of a statue. This is its *formal cause,* its essence. The formal cause may perhaps be understood as the logical content of an object, such as could be recorded on the computer tape of an automatic machine programmed to produce it. Thirdly, there is the action which is directly responsible for the particular becoming - as the sculptor's hands and chisel fashion the block of marble. This is the *efficient cause* of the statue; the efficient cause of the child is his father. We also ask for the efficient causes of events and phenomena. So the efficient cause of an eclipse of the moon is the shadow of the earth, and the efficient cause of the light shining from the lantern is the pores in the shield through which pass the fine light particles ('if this is the way light is propagated'). Finally, any human action is directed to an end - what did he do it for? - and this is the *final cause;* and as human action is analogous to that of nature we must also look for the final causes of natural objects and events.

Definitions are, of course, neither true nor false, and we must not blame Aristotle for using the same word *(aitia)* for his four kinds of causes. We would not ask for the cause of a statue, or of a child, though we may ask for the cause of a pregnancy. We do find sense in talking of final causes, even if we deny that they are relevant in the physical world. On the other hand, the relation between force and motion which, since Galileo we take as a prototype of the cause-effect relation, is not included in Aristotle's scheme.

The Aristotelian types of answers to the questions why and how do not add up to a complete specification of the situation, any more so than Socrates' causes or the ideas of primitive man. Aristotle's questions refer to particular aspects of the situation under test, and the answers are meant to pick out the salient point. We answer causal questions in the same way. When, e.g. we ask how Hitler died, we do not want to know the anatomy or the physiology of death, or the political history leading to his death, but are satisfied with the answer that he was shot by his henchmen. Perhaps we may require some enlargement of this statement, but we do not require a molecular or biological analysis. A complete answer in this sense would fail to answer the specific question, which is based on a specific interest of the questioner. Aristotle's explanation of the eclipse is perfectly satisfactory, but it is not anywhere near to a complete astronomical analysis of the situation.

As answers to particular questions Aristotle's cause and effect relations do not lend themselves to constructions of chains of relations of the type: A caused B, then B caused C, etc., i.e. to chains which extend from a grey past to a distant future. Such constructions would be futile in the light of the great variety of phenomena which must be explained.

The cause, in particular the effecient cause, should precede the effect. But, asks Aristotle, how can it act, if, preceding the effect, it has ceased to be before the effect has appeared? In the limiting case, the cause is simultaneous with the effect, as in the example of the eclipse. Aristotle thought that normally the effect waxes as the cause wanes. The temporal contiguity must be preserved under all conditions. Different causes can have the same effect, though the effect will always be the effect of its cause. But between the beginning of the action of the cause and its completion some other cause can intervene so that the prediction of an effect from its cause is always uncertain. (This reasoning, incidentally, looks like a valid argument against those who propose to equate causality with predictability.)

The question why? is however not always justified, because some things exist, or come into existence, *by nature*. Animals and their organs, plants and the elementary substances, these and their likes we say exist *by nature* - they have within themselves a principle of change and stability. *Nature* is the principle and cause of motion and stability in those of her creatures in which she inheres primarily. Any attempt to prove this would be childish. On the other hand, when a cause exists, there is normally no doubt what it is. If I hold my hands over a candle and burn my fingers, or if I push a ball and it moves, I know the cause of the pain or the movement.

Sometimes however we do not readily find a cause when we seek one. Some older authors, Aristotle mentions, have included chance amongst the possible causes.

But what is it that is properly called chance, or luck or misfortune? Aristotle disagrees with Empedocles' theory of evolution (which has recently been revived by Monod (1970).) According to Empedocles, nature first produced at random parts of animals and all kinds of combinations of these parts, such as 'man-faced oxen'. But separate legs or heads and odd combinations were not capable of life or propagation, so that the present forms were established by natural selection. The very constancy of present forms, argued Aristotle, speaks against Empedocles' theory of random creation. Cause-effect relations are linear sequences, but it can happen that two independent sequences of events come together in time and place with spectacular results: these are what we call fortuitous, coincidental. Irregular and exceptional consequences - Aristotle meditates - may then occur, and what we call luck or chance corresponds to some reality and is not mere fiction. He illustrates this idea by cases such as this: a man goes to the market in order to sell a pig, and surprises a bad debtor in the act of receiving payment and so is able to lay his hand on the money; or a sick person has his hair cut and finds that the exposure of his bare scalp to sunshine cures him. In general, Aristotle maintains there can be no incidental causation unless there exists a causal sequence to which it is incidental. Aristotle also calls incidental those features of an occurrence which are irrelevant to it. A house is going up because the builder works, but the builder may also, incidentally, have a fair complexion.

Aristotle's causes account for some aspects of a situation, his contingencies for others. It appears that situations and events are neither completely controlled by causes nor completely incidental. Different aspects require different interpretations to which Aristotle has presented the keys; the same feature may be accidental from one point of view and causally conditioned from another. He does not attempt to weave together the different ways of explaining events into one comprehensive scheme. Aristotle's pluralism, allowing for a variety of influences, has certainly contributed to the acceptance of his theory of cause and effect for two thousand years by philosophers who perhaps would question some of his other ideas, by the Church, and by physicists who in practice operate the pluralistic Aristotelian approach when explaining the results of their experiments.

One more aspect of Aristotle's theory should be mentioned. Aristotle connected the logic of explanation with the factual relation between cause and effect because for him explaining an event meant finding its cause. Explanations, he said, have the form of a syllogism where the cause is the middle term (the term which disappears in the conclusion). For instance, why does the moon suffer an eclipse? The answer is spelt out as a syllogism as follows: The earth comes between the sun and the moon: the earth obstructs the light of the sun, therefore the moon receives no sunlight, i.e. it suffers an eclipse.

However much Aristotle contributed to learning in general, and in spite of the fact that one of his major books is entitled Physics, he was not innovative in what we now mean by physics. The foundation of theoretical physics should be attributed rather to *Democritus (460-370)* who had died before Aristotle was born. None of Democritus' books survive, and he is known only through references made to him by other writers - Aristotle himself refers to him frequently. It is now generally recognised not only that the atomic theory as outlined by Democritus is essentially correct, but also that the reasoning that led him to it is entirely valid: it was accepted by Newton (Vavilov, 1946).

The mobility of matter, its transformations, its discreteness and its ability to be broken down into tiny parts lead to the conclusion that matter is made up of small units. The observed qualities of matter, like colours or sounds, are only appearances, they exist by convention; its atoms are indestructible, immutable, imperceptible, solid, impenetrable and indivisible. There cannot be an infinite variety of these, otherwise the number of possible combinations would be infinitely large, and thus the probability of a repetition of forms and shapes infinitely small. But we observe everywhere repetitions; rocks and plants fall into recognisable groups, children are similar to their parents. Aristotle compared atoms with the letters of the alphabet, each of which has its own shape but which can be arranged in various positions or orders. In nature there is nothing but atoms and void space. Democritus was, of course, not able to estimate the dimensions of atoms and he did not know that the empty space in which the atoms move would be found to have distinctive properties such as the ability to sustain electric and magnetic fields. But he drew from the reduction of everything to atoms and empty space the conclusion that the events of this world occur in a strictly determined way, by necessity, because the movement of atoms with a limited number of properties would be controlled by simple rules such as those of attraction and collision. The resulting aggregations determine all qualities so that 'Nothing comes by itself, everything occurs by necessity and reason'.

There is, unfortunately, no knowing what precisely Democritus understood by necessity. Obviously the term 'necessity' does not convey exactly the same idea as the Greek term $\alpha\nu\alpha\gamma\kappa\eta$. A result may be necessary because we relate it to the general rule. This logical connotation is absent from the Greek word, which is restricted to the interpretation of natural events, as controlled by fate or a rule of nature. But Democritus cannot have had an idea of what we call laws of nature. So having conceived the idea of atoms, Democritus could not make it fertile. That had to wait for the advent of a quantitative chemistry.

Aristotle's causality and Democritus' determinism and concept of necessity both had the function of explaining how nature works, and the relation between these concepts has been much studied. It has, for instance, been argued that causality in the Aristotelian sense differs only formally from determinism, or, alternatively, that causality denotes a principle of unique generation much narrower than determinism, or that causation is one of several categories of determinism, others being quantitative self-determination or inertia, interaction, etc. But there is no doubt that the Aristotelian idea contains elements which do not fit into the Democritean scheme and vice versa. Aristotle's causes are specific answers to specific questions and do not imply necessity; Democritus' necessity affirms that the state of the world tomorrow is firmly rooted in the state of the world today.

2
Freedom and God's Foresight

Epicurus (342-270) was 20 years old when Aristotle died. Again, no original works of Epicurus survive, but to judge by later references they were widely studied by his contemporaries. Epicurus accepted the Democritean doctrines and supplemented them by a theory of chance. Apart from that, he considered them from a psychotherapeutic angle - showing that a materialistic explanation of events liberates humanity from the fear of divine wrath or evil spirits.

In the Middle Ages Epicurus was mainly known and defamed as the godless one; a basic knowledge of his theory of chance was familiar to scientists at least up to the time of Kepler. It seems then to have got lost in the reconstruction of physics by Galileo and Newton.

The Epicurean criticism of atomistic determinism can be interpreted and summarised as follows: Epicurus adhered to the Democritean atomic theory but he objected to the idea of complete necessity.

Let us assume, he argued, that the movements of the atoms are rigorously controlled by necessity and that the atoms and their movements control everything else. Then no moral or logical proposition, the Democritean theory included, can claim to be valid. For any proposition must exist in the symbolic form of spoken words or of marks on paper. These symbols - say sequences of compression or expansion of air - are natural, physical events and as such, according to Democritus, fully determined atomic motions. All atomic motions are real, none are more real than others, so that the proposition that atoms and space exist cannot have more reality than its negation. Unless we maintain a discrimination between true propositions and false propositions and assert the superiority of the true proposition over the false one, no theory can be better than any other. Again, the morally good and noble deed is as natural as the foulest crime, and if natural sequences fully determine our actions, no one could rightly be praised or blamed. Therefore, the validity of a proposition or the value of a deed must have a source or reason different from the sequence of motions of the atoms; but whatever this source may be, it can act only if a loophole is left for it in the material world, and atomic movements are not always fully determined by necessity. The deterministic sequences cannot be without gaps.

Epicurus therefore suggests that sometimes there occur deviations of the atomic motions, which he calls the clinamen and which are alternative to free fall and collision. Let me quote from his interpreter, *Lucretius (98-55)*: 'If the elementary particles do not make by swerving a beginning of motion such as to break the decrees of fate, so that cause may not follow cause to infinity, whence comes this free will in living creatures all over the earth?' Or from *Cicero (106-43)*; who complains that Epicurus 'by making atoms swerve is entertaining simultaneously two utterly inexplicable propositions, one that something takes place without a cause ... the other that when two atoms are travelling one moves in a straight line and the other swerves.' Elsewhere, Cicero says that the Epicureans teach that 'those who bring in an everlasting series of causes rob the human mind of free will and fetter it in the chain of a fated necessity. In addition to gravity and impact there arises a third form of motion when the atoms swerve sideways a minimal space (termed by Epicurus $\epsilon\lambda\alpha\gamma\iota\sigma\tau o\nu$). This swerving takes place without cause, otherwise we could have no freedom whatever since the movement of the mind was controlled by the movement of the atom.'

Or: 'If everything were fate, assent also would be given by necessity and there would be no justice in praise or blame, honours or punishment.'

The particular way by which Epicurus introduces chance is tied to his simple idea of atoms normally moving in free fall, and colliding with each other. During the free movement random deviations occur which provide the required element of chance. Modern analogues to Epicurus will be quoted below. Epicurus' clinamen is a kind of event quite different from the Aristotelian coincidence. It is fundamental, absolutely irreducible chance, which cannot be further analysed or explained.

We are, however, given no idea how reason or moral judgement act where mechanical necessity fails. Epicurus' reasoning, though not easily refuted, has therefore not often been accepted as a proof of indeterminism. It has been argued that strict causality is not incompatible with moral judgement and true statements. Other authors have considered free will and truth utterly problematic propositions.

Christianity. Boetius

The advent of Christianity, with its new concept of divinity, added another problem to the cause-effect-necessity-chance complex. *Boetius (480-525)*, at the cross-roads of the Classical and the Medieval worlds, gave in his *Consolation of Philosophy* a lucid account of the difficulty of reconciling man's responsibility for his deeds, good and evil, i.e. his free will, with the existence of the Christian God who knows and foreknows and directs everything. The Epicurean philosophy of atoms, necessity and random events, could give no guidance to a Christian thinker. On the other hand, classical tragedy had taught that men are subject to fate, and the Greek and Roman custom of consulting oracles and signs had raised questions of human freedom. The later Stoics had derived their faith in fate and the validity of divination from their belief in the unity of nature and God. But whereas fate, oracles and signs were never considered as comprehensive, and Epicurus alleviated necessity by the clinamen, the Christian God could not be allowed to leave any gaps. Boetius, therefore, devalued Aristotle's acceptance of chance and raised his individual cause-effect sequences into an all-pervading network of sequences, into chains of close-knit causes, a necessity through which God's foresight is realised in the world. Aristotle, wisely, had abstained from combining causes in this way. Boetius had to accept the mystery of a complete network of causes a mystery which afterwards was rarely questioned.

'If chance is defined as an event produced by random motion without any causal nexus, I would say there is not such thing as chance. If God imposes order upon all things there is no opportunity for random events.'

And: 'Whenever something is done for some purpose, and for certain reasons something other than what was intended happens, it is called chance. We may therefore define chance as an unexpected event due to the conjunction of its causes with action which is done for some purpose. The conjunction and coincidence of the cause is effected by that order which proceeds by the inescapable nexus of causation, descending from the fount of Providence and ordering all things in their own time and place'. 'But is there room in this chain of close-knit causes for any freedom of the will? The two seem clean contrary and opposite: God's universal foreknowledge and freedom of the will'.

Boetius solves the paradox - which had earlier already impressed itself on educated Jews and Christians - as follows: The difference between an event which is due to the action of free will and an event that is causally necessary rests in the mystery of time. Facing the future, we believe ourselves to have in some respects a choice, but we cannot alter the past. We may see a man deliberating and acting, and when we have seen him, we know what he did regardless of the circumstances of his free choice, but our knowledge did not diminish his freedom or responsibility.

Now God created the world, space and time and the 'state of God is ever that of eternal presence; His knowledge, too, transcends all temporal change and abides in the immediacy of His presence. It embraces all the infinite recesses of past and future and views them in the immediacy of its knowing as though they are happening in the present. If you wish to consider the foreknowledge or prevision by which he discovers all things, it will be more correct to think of it not as a kind of foreknowledge of the future, but as the knowledge of a never-ending presence.' For God, it seems, the world is what Minkowski calls the space-time continuum. And no more than a member of an audience, on his lower level, by his presence in the theatre, can be said to restrict freedom of the actor, does the divine intelligence by its timeless presence tie a free deliberation to a causal nexus.

Boetius places the error of those who 'think that the necessity of events is consequent upon their being foreseen' in a wrong theory of knowledge. 'Everything that is known is comprehended not according to its own nature, but according to the ability to know of those who do the knowing'.

Boetius's Consolation was, next to the gospels, the most influential book of the Middle Ages. The compatibility with God's almighty knowledge and foresight of human free will, of man's responsibility and his liberty to act in conformity with God's will or to sin, became one of the major problems of theology and philosophy. Ingenious, profound or absurd solutions were discussed. *Duns Scotus (1265-1308)* and Jewish philosophers like *Nahmias (14th century)* thought a solution of the antinomy between God's foresight and human responsibility beyond human power.

Nahmias writes: although we cannot understand this great mystery, for 'everything is foreseen' and 'freedom of choice is granted', seems like a contradiction, nevertheless do not question this matter. We are unable to grasp this mystery as it is written 'for My thoughts are not your thoughts, neither are your ways My ways'.

Duns Scotus, on the basis of Aristotelian ideas, distinguished between natural causes, free causes and casual causes.

Natural causes, i.e., causes in the usual sense, may be recognised as self-evident, and awareness of the cause provides a more certain knowledge than the experiences of the effect alone. A small number of instances is sufficient to show which events have a natural cause, and will always follow this cause. For what happens in most cases does not proceed from a free cause but is the natural effect of the cause. Deliberate choice is a free cause and does not produce the same effect again and again. A casual cause produces its effect owing to some unusual circumstances. If an acorn brings forth an oak tree, it is the natural cause of that tree; but if a lamb is born with two heads this is due to a casual cause. A free cause is an intelligent decision. In classifying causes Scotus has clearly raised the question of how to recognise causes and answered it by reference to induction.

Causal necessity does not preclude free will. If someone voluntarily hurls himself over a precipice and, while falling, all the time continues to will it, he indeed falls by the necessity of natural gravity and yet he freely wills that fall. Liberty belongs to the perfection of volition. Will, in the proper sense, is not natural inclination. There is in man a natural inclination to beatitude but it does not follow that the will, as free, necessarily and perpetually desires this last end, nor that it necessarily elicits a conscious and deliberate act in regard to that object. Every elicited act of the will is free, and an act is praiseworthy or blameworthy as it proceeds from the free will.

An act is morally good if it is free and objectively good and done with the right intention in the right way. But the intellect is not, like the will, a free power, as it is not in the power of the intellect to restrain its assent to the truth which it apprehends.

Scotus thus draws the dividing line between causation and freedom differently from Epicurus. According to Scotus only the volition, in a carefully defined and restricted sense, can be called free; judgement is not subject to outside influences and is not free, because we have no freedom of choice about facts and reasons and about what is true, so that an all-pervading divine power can endanger moral liberty only.

But an all-pervading atomic necessity is in conflict with both moral liberty and intellectual reasoning.

·

3

The Scientific Age

Technological progress during the Middle Ages was considerable, but intellectual interest was focused on matters spiritual and divine. So that the image of physics and the physicist remained what it was at the end of the classical era:- that of an abstract ontology founded on the study of essences and operating by syllogistic deduction. The persistence of these ideas is well illustrated in a book in which *Kepler (1571-1630)* described and explained the appearance of a nova in 1604, *De stella nova in pede serpentarii (1606)*. This nova was not only exceptionally bright but also it occurred at the place and time of a great conjunction, so that the astrologers had already made forecasts of world-shaking events. Kepler does not accept the claims of the astrologers, but he is still worried about the coincidence of the nova with the great conjunction. Not concealing his pride in being an astronomer rather than a physicist, he discusses in detail the opinions of three groups of physicists and rejects them all.

The first group, which he obviously least dislikes, makes a world spirit responsible. The second group are the Epicureans. According to the Epicurean physicists, not only is the coincidence accidental, but also the star itself was formed from atoms by chance. The Epicureans argue that in the course of time everything possible must occur, just as in a game of dice all possible combinations will turn up. For the third (Aristotelian) sect, neither the conjunction of the planets nor the fire of the nova were accidental but had astronomical and physical causes respectively; only their coming together was a particular coincidence.

But what is chance, Kepler asks, with reference to the Epicureans. 'Of course, a detestable idol and nothing else but an insult to God high and almighty, as God, the author of the world, placed the nova into the sky for the edification of man.' Even the mathematics of the Epicureans is wrong, because some combinations need never arise. And after all, 'why does Venus come up in one throw, and in the next one Dog? Of course, the player has thrown the dice from the other side, or commenced with the other hand or shook them differently. There is nothing which lacks a cause if somebody would take into account these subtle conditions'. The Aristotelian view, argues Kepler, is less objectionable but is also not credible. Perhaps the star would have arisen at the time of the great conjunction - perhaps; but it is not likely that mere coincidence would also have made it occupy the special location where it was seen. Considering all this, the theological view should be accepted that the coincidence was ordained by God to advise man of His might.

Although Kepler was a contemporary of Galileo and in correspondence with him, his physics - he never called himself a physicist - was still medieval. It is remarkable how clearly he discriminated between the Aristotelian and the Epicurean ideas and how familiar he was with the theory of atoms.

Atomism, though not precisely in the sense of Democritus, had found an advocate in *Giordano Bruno (1548-1600)* and had become a much discussed topic: 'When a young enquirer wished to defend the atomic theory against the Aristotelian physics in a public disputation in Paris (1624), the theological faculty denounced as heretical the doctrine that everything consists of atoms, since it contradicted the catholic doctrine of the Eucharist. The disputation was forbidden at the last moment, after nearly 1000 people had assembled to hear it.' (Höffding (1900), Vol. 1, 215). The foremost representative of atomism in the 17th century was *Pierre Gassendi (1592-1655)* who revived the classical doctrine to such an extent as to accustom the theological world to the idea that atomism is not necessarily a godless doctrine, and prepared the way for Newton's concept of particles.

With Galileo, and even more with Newton on the one hand, and with Torricelli, Viviani, Pascal and Guericke on the other hand, a new concept of physics was born. Both sides were emphatic about the need to observe and to experiment. The former were the founders of a mathematical physics in which the cause-effect relation tends to be replaced by laws of nature; the latter were experimentally, in the first instance qualitatively, studying the causes of effects, newly observed or known through contemporary technology.

Causes of observed effects

The miners' pump presented a problem. With the development of mining in the late Middle Ages the technology of pumping water out of mines had become a recognised subject for inventions. *Agricola (1494-1555)*, in his famous book *De Re Metallica (1556)*, could list three different types of such pumps, with a considerable number of patterns of each type which he illustrated, more or less clearly, in attractive woodcuts. One sees a curious combination of advanced ideas with primitive artisanship. Iron and other metals were used very sparingly and in rather crude shapes; tubes, cylinders and pistons were mainly wooden, with sewn leather cones where a water-tight fit was required. The majority of these pumps were operated by hand, others were driven by water or animal power.

In a suction pump the cylinder has at its bottom a valve which permits water to rise into it but prevents it from flowing back; the piston has a similar valve. When a piston is raised, water is sucked up through a pipe from a sump several feet below the cylinder; when the piston is lowered the water in the cylinder passes into the space above the piston; this water is ejected through an opening at the top of the cylinder at the next ascent of the piston. The length of the feed pipes was limited by leakage due to the primitive workmanship. A hundred years later, in Galileo's time, with improved engineering, the leakage was reduced and longer feedpipes were tried. Still it was found impossible to pass a thirty foot limit. What was the cause of this limit? The cause of sucking used to be explained as due to nature's *horror vacui,* that is, nature was believed not to admit any space left free of matter so that the water lifted by the piston had to be replaced by water taken out of the sump. But why should this *horror* of nature cease at thirty feet? *Torricelli (1608-1647)*, a student of Galileo, found a better explanation. He suggested that the atmosphere exerted a pressure everywhere, pushing the water up into the space vacated by the raised piston, the pressure being equal to that of thirty feet of water. This idea was strikingly confirmed by Viviani in 1643, who showed that atmospheric pressure supported a mercury column which had the same weight as thirty feet of water, however long the space was above it: Viviani had invented the barometer. The *experimentum crucis* was carried out by *Pascal (1623-1662)*, who in 1647 showed that the length of the mercury column was about 7 cm shorter on the top of the Puy-de-Dôme than at the bottom.

This case-history exemplifies a cause-effect logic used ever since in the experimental sciences. An effect is found, a cause, or several possible causes, are guessed. Then the conditions under which the effect is observed are varied and the guess is confirmed or disproved. The conclusion can of course be upset by new thoughts and experiments; man can err. In this sense it has been argued that an *experimentum crucis* does not exist. Such cause-effect relations belong to Aristotle's class of efficient causes. The novelty consists in the quantitative aspect and the particular effort made to find the true cause: finding the cause had become a serious research effort.

Galileo (1564-1642) may be called the inventor of laws of physics. He was guided by the idea that simple phenomena obey simple rules, in particular that a simple mathematical formula must exist by which the relation between the distance travelled by a body in free fall and the duration of the fall can be expressed. He reasoned that it is not necessarily profitable to examine the 'causes' of these phenomena. Galileo did not merely propose a new idea of what physics should be, he carried it out and demonstrated it in practice. He has been praised for it, but he was also criticised and attacked not only by partisans of the old order but also by moderns for leaving the door open for the return of Aristotelian prejudices.

Galileo's innovation of a combination of experiment and mathematics was not appreciated by his contemporaries. Even less appreciated was his other revolutionary innovation: the attention to detail, which may have been regarded as undignified in classical antiquity. Descartes, while rightly considering himself a scientist, was apparently not aware that Galileo had also extended the law of inertia and discussed atomism; Descartes complained that Galileo was describing facts without giving their causes, and wrote about him: 'He has only investigated the reasons of some particular effects and has therefore built without foundation.' Indeed, playing with rolling balls must have appeared a time-wasting, trivial affair to a philosopher concerned with the essence of the world, but it was Galileo who, by introducing the idea of laws of physics, paved the way for a physical understanding of Democritean necessity.

Descartes (1596-1650) began by inquiring into the basis of irrefutable knowledge, and it was, as Brunschvicg points out, his great merit to have established confidence in scientific truth. This was not demanded of Epicurean physics and it was not inspired by what science offered in the Middle Ages and in the Renaissance. Descartes was a physicist, a mathematician and a philosopher.

In the footsteps of Beeckman (1588-1637), a Dutch physicist, he enunciated a law of conservation of motion because 'God has created matter together with the motion and the rest of its parts ..... he keeps as much motion and rest in the universe now as he put in when he created it .....' If a material body has once commenced to move it continues to move with equal force until other bodies stop it or retard it. All moving bodies tend to continue to move in a straight line. Of all the various changes which Aristotle had discussed, Descartes retained only the movement of bodies from place to place, as the only material change which can be envisaged clearly. Only change of motion requires a cause, and this cause is another motion. The whole material world is reducible to extended, divisible, mobile bodies, operating like the wheels of a clock. The material world, and this is for Descartes a mechanical world, *is* a clockwork. The qualities which we observe are constructions of the senses. Causes are mechanical links. It is intuitively clear, thought Descartes, how one bar pushes another bar, how one cogwheel turns the next; the effect is of the same nature as the cause, and hence contains no more and no less matter or movement than the cause, and 'out of nothing nothing comes.'

Independent of the material world, but not less substantial, is the world of the mind. How then do these two substances, matter and mind, interact; in particular, how does the mind or the soul affect the body? Descartes had satisfied himself that the properties of matter cannot include the capacity of producing thought and that consciousness cannot produce matter. But although consciousness and matter are self-sufficient, independent substances, they work together in man. This is incomprehensible and contradicts the principles of conservation. Descartes wondered if the soul could change the direction of a moving body without affecting its speed. He suggested also that the pineal gland is involved in the collaboration of body and mind, a curious idea, rightly ridiculed by contemporary and later authors. But the dualism lived on and made Epicurus' query incomprehensible. Epicurus, as a monist, wondered how the mind could be free, as atomic movements controlled every detail in this world. Then Boetius, as a theological monist, substituted God for the Democritean atoms. Descartes, on the contrary, saw the problem not in the freedom of mind from matter but in their interdependence. In detaching the material world from the spiritual one, Descartes established the material world as an independent and un-restricted field of research.

Some of Descartes' followers went further than the master and queried if *any* causal relation could really be understood. Take for instance a collision between moving bodies. How does it work? *We* can study collisions with high speed cine cameras, and analyse the results of collisions with high-power microscopes, and if necessary with X-ray crystallographic methods. In the elastic case both bodies are first deformed until they have the same speed, then the elastic forces assert themselves and push the bodies apart while the original shapes are restored. In the inelastic case the deformation involves the breaking of crystals or crystallites, glide processes within the crystallites, irreversible transformation of mechanical energy into heat, etc. In either case the processes satisfy the rules of conservation of momentum and energy. All this of course was unknown - how right were the Cartesians not to understand what happens in a collision! The answers lay far ahead of their time. Still, here was a new and eventually tremendously fruitful approach to the problem of causality: not to be satisfied with assigning causes to effects but to understand how they work. No wonder that theologically inclined students proposed to see in any observed connection an individual act of God, so that on each occasion God dispenses the effect to follow the cause. (Geulinx, Malebranche, Glanville.)

For *Spinoza (1632-1677)* the principle of causation was self-evident, illuminating everything else - a view with which Aristotle would have agreed. Causes - which Spinoza conceived as product-ive of the effect - correspond to premises from which we draw conclusions. In the last resort, the cause of all things is God. It is here of interest, as confirming Spinoza's reliance on the Aristotel-ian concept of causality, to note that Spinoza carries out this dis-cussion in the 'Short Treatise on God, Man and his Well-being' in terms of the extensive classification of causes provided by Burgersdijk's Logic, which in his time was a highly popular book. (Appendix A)

Spinoza did not search for a causal relation between mind and matter, as he took both matter (extension) and consciousness to be attributes of one and the same universal substance or God; this does not, however, imply that the one attribute can readily be related to the other. Spinoza's unity of mind and matter was more inspiring to the life-sciences and to poets than it was to physicists.

Leibniz (1646-1716) was, like Descartes, a great mathematician; like Spinoza, he thought in terms of a unity of mind and body.

He gave a prominent place to the principle of sufficient reason. This is neither a principle of formal logic nor deduced from experience: 'Nothing occurs without there being a reason why it should be so and not otherwise'. Leibniz derives from this principle the idea of an equality of antecedent and consequence. Without this equality, the world would permanently be either in a state of progression or in a state of regression. Unfortunately the whole early history of the principles of conservation is bedevilled by an indefinite terminology, as the concepts on which they are based, like speed and velocity, had not yet been clarified. So on the one hand Leibniz followed Galileo in understanding force to be the product of mass and the square of the speed, and concluded from Galileo's experiments · that it is this quantity which is conserved; on the other hand Leibniz talked about force as the product of mass and velocity, a quantity which we call momentum, and which was what was conserved according to Descartes. Equality of cause and effect demands, Leibniz thought, that conservation of this quantity must include the direction of motion, while Descartes had played with the idea that the mind can influence the direction without violating the mechanical conservation principle. Leibniz' views on the unity of mind and matter made such a distinction unnecessary.

Newton (1642-1727). According to Duhem, Parisian scholars from the early 14th century onwards argued as to whether or not there.exists a difference between celestial and sub-lunar physics, i.e., the physics of the stars and that applying to changes on earth. This question was finally settled by Descartes and Newton, in particular through Newton's discovery that the laws of acceleration and gravitation hold everywhere, a discovery arrived at by the interpretation of observations and experiments carried out by Kepler, Galileo and others.

The third book of the *Principia* is introduced by rules for philosophy. The fourth rule, added in the third edition (1726), reads as follows:

'In experimental philosophy we are to look upon propositions inferred by general induction from phenomena as accurately true or as good approximations, notwithstanding any contrary hypotheses which may have been put forward, till such time as other phenomena occur by which they either may be made more accurate or found subject to exceptions.

'This rule we must follow that the argument of induction may not be evaded by hypotheses'.

Relevant here also are rules one and two.

Rule I: 'Do not give more causes of natural events than are both true and sufficient for the explanation of the phenomena. The philosophers teach: nature does nothing in vain, and it would be vain to use more effort than necessary. For nature is simple and does not luxuriate in unnecessary causes.'

Rule II: 'Hence, the same cause must be assigned to natural effects of the same kind, as far as possible; examples are, breathing in man and animals; the free fall in Europe and in America; the light emitted by a fire and that coming from the sun; the reflection of light on earth and on the planets.'

In the light of these rules, let us look at Newton's famous axioms or laws of motion *(axiomata sive leges motus)* with which the first book begins.

Law I: Every body perseveres in its state of rest, or of uniform motion in a straight line unless it is compelled to change that state by forces impressed on it.

Law II: The change of motion (momentum) is proportional to the force applied, and takes place in the straight line in which that force acts.

Law III: An action is always opposed by an equal reaction, or, the mutual actions of two bodies are always equal and act in opposite directions.

So physics and astronomy, now united, are based on laws and these laws stem from experience. The laws apply to bodies which need not, but may be atoms, in the Democritean sense. In fact, Newton went to great trouble to find out how the gravitational forces depended on the shape of the bodies.

The great success of Newton's theories promoted the tendency to think in terms of Epicurean necessity expressed as laws rather than in terms of Aristotelian causes. Malebranche (1638-1715) wrote: Let us leave to metaphysics the study of efficient causes of things; science must be content with studying their laws.

Newton himself, however, did not gladly and not everywhere resign from the search for causes, as is apparent from his first and second rules. The forces which deflect bodies from a straight path can be taken as efficient causes in the Aristotelian sense as well as elements of a Democritean necessity. Amongst forces gravitation plays a supreme role. Now, what is, and what causes, gravitation? Newton, and many of his contemporaries, meditated about the cause of gravitation. The Cartesians, who thought in purely kinematical terms, suspected it to be a reactionary idea. Was Newton, by postulating action at a distance, re-introducing bodies with souls of an intelligence so high that they not only knew instantly what happened a long distance away, but also how to influence these distant bodies? Newton had no explanation to offer, at least no physical explanation. Hence his famous dictum that he would not invent hypotheses.

Particular aspects of the new science were emphasised by *d'Alembert (1717-1783)* and by *Laplace (1749-1827)*.

D'Alembert rightly criticised Leibniz' axiom of the proportionality of cause and effect for its lack of precision. He also asked whether Newtonian physics was just a summary of observations and experience and as such 'contingent', or whether the laws had a rational foundation. We, encouraged by the progress of science which every one can see through the advances of technology, are only too inclined to trust the expert without querying how he gets his evidence. In the 18th century scientists at least were often less trusting. If a rule was said to be derived from a number of observations, might not the next observation upset it? Only Euclidean geometry based on rational and precisely formulated axioms had stood the test of time, and was therefore widely regarded as prototype of a real science. Hence the tendency to look at Newton's physics as an extension of Euclidean geometry. D'Alembert also pointed out that electrical phenomena such as attraction, or the excitation of nerves, are not covered by dynamics. The world is one and a true science should throw its light on all causes and all effects.

Laplace shared with most mathematical physicists of the period the conviction that the world is controlled by a complete set of rigorous laws. He formulated this idea as follows:

'All events, even those which seem to be too insignificant to have any relation to the grand laws of nature, follow each other with no less necessity than the revolutions of the solar system. In ignorance of the ties which they have with the whole universe, they were thought to depend on final causes, or on chance ... but such imaginary causes have by and by been pushed back as our knowledge extended ..... as we learn that nothing can commence without a cause which made it .... we must therefore think of the present state of the universe as the effect of its previous state and as a cause of the next one. An intelligence which at the given instant knew all the forces acting in nature and corresponding positions of the body, an intelligence which is moreover wide enough to analyse these data - such an intelligence could give in one formula the movements of the largest bodies in the universe together with those of the smallest atoms; nothing would remain uncertain for this intelligence, and the future and the past would be open before his eyes. The human spirit finds a feeble sketch of this intelligence in the perfection which it could give to astronomy. The discoveries in mechanics and in geometry, together with that of the universal gravitation have enabled it to comprise in one analytical expression the past and future state of the solar system .... Progress in the search for the truth brings the human spirit steadily nearer to the intelligence which has been described - but this will always remain infinitely far away.'

This statement, or part of it, has often been quoted as the gospel of the deterministic view of the world. It was perhaps more representative of 17th century thinking - Leibniz had considered the existence of such a supreme intelligence - than of that of Laplace's contemporaries. Laplace did not mean that Newton's laws alone determined everything. Too much was known in his time about chemical and electrical phenomena. He must have been aware of the difficulty, pointed out by Leibniz, which his construction would encounter if the world, and the number of atoms in it, were not taken as finite. The construction has also been criticized (Cassirer 1956) as self-contradictory:

if the intelligence could be thought to work discursively, i.e. gathering information and applying laws to it, the process would take time, however short, so that the conditions needed for the forecast of knowing all the forces at a given instant, cannot be satisfied. On the other hand, the intelligence cannot be thought to operate intuitively, because then Laplace's reasoning would not apply as it is based on an extension of Newton's dynamics. Laws, such as those stated by Newton, are not found in nature like nuggets of gold picked up in a stream, but they exist in the mind of the observer who applies them to natural phenomena.

But Laplace had clearly stated that we are not likely to encounter his 'intelligence'. He would also have agreed that it, or he, is only a symbol for the completeness of the links between successive states of the universe. The idea that the course of nature is fully determined in advance remained the creed of the scientist until the first quarter of the 20th century.

The 17th century saw also the beginning of another science destined to modify the ideas of cause and chance. *Pascal, Fermat, Huygens, J. Bernoulli* and others laid the foundations of the theory of probability. Their problems had, with one exception, nothing to do with physics. Probability theory was not applied to physics until the 19th century. Chance was studied first in relation to game theory, and secondly as a matter for underwriters in the insurance business. Later, probability theory was applied to the evaluation of the effect of inoculations. The exception mentioned was the application of the theory to the distribution of the planetary planes and of stars.

As the mathematical theory of probability expanded, the meaning of probability was queried again and again. *Coolidge (1925)* quoted in this connection a definition of mathematics as the science in which we never know what we are talking about or what our results mean, so we should be wary. Objective and subjective interpretations of mobility have been given. The subjective one goes back to J. Bernoulli who defined probability as a measure of the strength of our expectation of a future event.

An objective definition goes as follows: 'An event can happen in a certain number of ways which are all equally likely. A certain proportion of these are classed as favourable. The ratio of the number of favourable ways to the total number is called the probability that the event will turn out favourably.' This definition is too narrow, but in principle it covers the whole field of mathematical probability. The important point is that it is not asked why ways are equally likely. They may be so for quite trivial reasons, or for a reason beyond our understanding. Neither definition is clear cut and both are probably even circular. Terms such as 'equally likely', and 'strength of expectation' may well conceal the idea of probability. Also, the subjective and objective aspects of probability can often co-exist, and in particular an objective probability can guide our expectations.

4

The Meaning of Causes

Locke and Hume

Many aspects of causality were discussed by 17th century scientists, but it was left to Locke and Hume to query its significance and the reliance we place on it. What can make one event force another event into being? Why do we rely on particular sequences of events?

Locke (1632-1704), denying the existence of chance, had considered the principle of causality to be an intuitive truth, confirmed by experience.

Hume (1711-1776) is credited by Höffding with having *established* 'the problem of causality - the problem on the solution of which every estimation of the significance of the exact sciences rests. At the root of all investigations lies the desire to discover what it is which holds the innermost parts of the world together.... It must be remembered, however, that Hume never doubted that we must continue to make constant use of the causal proposition both in theory and in practice; he only asks whether it can be *established*, and to this question he finds a negative answer'.

Hume had stated: 'I have just now examined one of the most supreme questions in philosophy, that concerning power and efficacy of causes'. He came to the conclusion that power and efficacy of causes are at best subjective impressions. It does not matter how these are expressed; the terms efficacy, agency, power, force, energy, necessity, connection, productive quality, are for him synonymous. Hume could see no logical or intuitive evidence for any type of causality, as we never have any impression that contains any power or efficacy, not even in actions of conscious willing. He saw that there is no self-contradiction in saying that some things begin without cause. Experience shows only that one event follows another, but does not exhibit to us the inner necessity of the union which is what is meant by a causal relation.

But experience also shows us a tendency on the part of our ideas mutually to elicit each other. For instance, if we think of hunger we may think of thirst, if of thunder, of lightning. Every idea has an associative tendency, which in particular is satisfied by the cause-effect relation. We cannot explain or understand why or how consciousness has this inclination to associate different sense impressions, and to take its own inner states for external, objective phenomena. These facts, however, are the basis of our belief in a causal relation between things in the world, which thus exists in us rather than in the objects, and is a response to our own psychologically-based tendency to move from one impression or idea to another. Necessity is subjective, just as are the sense-qualities space and time.

This associative tendency leaves no room for chance. 'There is no such thing as chance in the world. Our ignorance of the real causes of any event has the same influence on the understanding.' Chance is for Hume nothing real in itself and, properly speaking, is merely the negation of a cause, its influence on the mind is contrary to that of causation, it leaves imagination indifferent and destroys the determination of the mind to survey certain subjects. No chance can be superior to another. Chance and causation are directly contrary, one hazard can be superior to another only by an admixture of causes. Remarks like these confirm that Hume never queried causality as such, but only its origin and the assignment of particular relations; it is of these that we have no proof. So he arrives at the definition: cause = an object precedent in time and contiguous to another, and regularly so united with it that the idea of the one determines the mind to form the idea of the other and the impression of the one to form a more lively idea of the other. This definition suggests no analysis of what experience really means and does not provide a foundation for discrimination between different types of causes. Hume summarises the rules by which the cause-effect relation is judged:

(1) contiguity in space and time,
(2) cause being prior to effect,
(3) constant union between cause and effect,
(4) same cause, same effect,
(5) if different objects produce the same effect, it is so by means of a common quality,
(6) difference in effect of two resembling causes proceeds from

that particular in which they differ.

(7) if any object increases with the increase of its cause, it is to be regarded as a compound effect.

(8) an object which exists for any time in its perfection without producing its effect is not the whole cause of that effect when it eventually occurs.

Hume cannot accept chance because he thinks in terms of Aristotelian causes; Aristotelian causes, as was shown above, admit chance only as lack of foresight. Hume, by reducing causality to the psychology of association, was bound to repeat what was implied by Aristotle. Hume's merit should be gauged in the light of contemporary ideas which were dominated by *Christian Wolff (1679-1754)*, an unimaginative but prolific follower of Leibniz. Wolff had claimed that the principle of causality could be derived from the logical principle of sufficient reason, curiously mixing up two different propositions, namely the logical one that it must be possible to give a sufficient reason for any statement, and the factual one that any event must have its cause. Hume exposed this solecism. He has been considered as a predecessor of Kant, who said that Hume awakened him from his dogmatic slumber, as well as of empiricists such as Maine de Biran, J.S. Mill and Dewey. Hume was not familiar with contemporary science - Kant has been criticised for relying too much on it.

Kant's (1724-1804) Critique of Pure Reason (Kritik der reinen Vernunft, 1781) is specifically an attempt to understand the world through the medium of physics and mathematics. How is science possible? The physics of the 18th century had three pillars which have since crumbled. They were the absolute space and time of Newton, the exclusive validity of Euclidean geometry, and strict causality. It is outside our scope to enquire how Kant's analysis could be adapted to the present situation.

Kant was as impressed by Hume's denial of a rational basis to the trust in causality as he was by the absolute validity of causal relations implied by Newton's physics and by the arguments of Leibniz and Descartes. Kant reconciles these ideas on the basis of an analysis of experience. Hume, he argued, was wrong in taking experience as something which is just given. It is, in fact, a long way from sensual data such as colours and sounds to the objects which we 'observe' and study. Objects, and the sciences, are objects and sciences for a subject; this subject is not an ego in a psychological sense but a 'consciousness' of a general type. The world as object of knowledge contains, according to Kant, elements which do not stem from sensual impressions. This is why the world can be described in logical terms, why it is controlled by geometry and subject to the passage of time in a regular manner. But the principle of sufficient reason cannot be made responsible for such *a priori* knowledge as we have of the world.

Experience, according to Kant, is possible only through the idea of a necessary tie *(Verknüpfung)* between perceptions. The first of these ties is the law of conservation of substance. The second is the principle of succession in time, the law of causality. All changes satisfy this law. We know *a priori* that any effect has a cause, but we learn only by experience what particular cause a particular event has had, or how long the time interval was between cause and effect. Time as such is never observed. I observe different objects at different times, but my observations do not necessarily provide objective evidence of what follows what, as we often observe in succession objects which exist simultaneously. We may for instance hear the warning note of a bird before we see the cat threatening the nest, but arguing that the cat caused the upheaval we conclude that the cat had arrived before the bird took fright. Only by applying the law of causality can we establish the direction of time, guided by the rule that the cause precedes the effect. Just as the *a priori* intuition of space is necessary to establish *objects* as such, so the law of causality establishes a *time frame* for everything we observe.

Kant's proof of causality is, of course, on a level very different from that of Wolff; it is based on the propositions that the effect cannot precede the cause and that there is no rigorous observational criterion for the temporal order of events. It was pointed out above that Aristotelian causality and Democritean necessity are not always distinguished and that it is the latter one which is implied in the Newtonian laws. Kant took his ideas of space, time and laws of nature from Newton, but in the proof of causality he obviously refers to events. This was pointed out in a somewhat quaint way by Ewing (1924) as follows:

'It is strictly correct to say, a true cause cannot be anything less than the whole previous state of the universe. But the practical and scientific application of the category of causality depends on our ability to sort out particular causal links. The proof of causality given, shows that we separate particular series from the whole.'

There is, as Eddington (1928) pointed out, another reason against connecting physical laws of the Newtonian type with the direction of time. Newtonian laws, like all laws we consider as fundamental, have mathematically the form of second order differential equations, that is, they refer to changes in time in such a way that they determine the intervals between states but not their order; for example, if a light signal can go from A to B, a signal can equally well go from B to A, but the arrival always follows the departure. (There exists another kind of physical law which was not known or appreciated in Kant's time and which implies the direction of time. This will be discussed below).

Causality is therefore not a particular law of physics but it makes physical and psychological laws possible. Consequently, Kant pronounces that nothing occurs by chance, that all changes take place according to the law of connection between cause and effect. In a later book (the *Kritik der Urteilskraft*) he comments that 'a system in which chance plays a role such as is attributed to Epicurus or Democritus, if taken literally, is so palpably absurd that it need not detain us'.

The step from a demonstration of causality as a constituent of the material world to a claim for its exclusive rule is, however, not an obvious one. Basically, Kant deduced the law of causality (or necessity) from the existence of an objective, ordered world. But, we may ask, does this exclude the possibility of irregularities? All human activity is, after all, carried out with the prospect of the unforeseen. And belief in miracles has not prevented people from crediting the world with order. Secondly, statistical explanations (which were unknown to Kant) have shown that the regular course of human-sized events is compatible with randomness on the molecular level.

As, according to Kant, it is the consciousness which imposes the law of causality on the objective world, Descartes' problem of the interaction of mind and matter is by-passed. Kant's solution does not, however, dispose of the Epicurean question concerning moral responsibility.

Kant refers to it as an 'antinomy of pure reason', a competition of transcendental ideas, the conflict between the thesis: 'Causality according to the laws of nature is not the only causality such that from it all phenomena could be derived. It is necessary to assume in addition the existence of a causality through freedom', and an equally convincing antithesis: 'There is no liberty but everything in the world comes solely according to the laws of nature'. But, teaches Kant, thesis and antithesis refer to different aspects of the world. The antithesis applies to the world as a scientific object, including man as an empirical self, the thesis to beings as things-in-themselves or as rational subjects *(noumena)*.

Even in Kant's lifetime the primacy of dynamics had begun to fade. With Buffon and Lamarck, Dalton, Lavoisier, Lomonosov, Rumford and Fourier, Franklin and Ampère, the life sciences, chemistry, the knowledge of electricity and heat increased fast, and the Newtonian system of forces and its mathematical elaboration were seen to cover only a small range of phenomena.

Comte (1798-1857). It was in the light of these new developments, in particular of Fourier's theory of heat, that August Comte, following Hume, developed the 'positivist' interpretation of science in general and causality in particular.

'Today', Comte wrote in 1835, 'all good minds recognise that real studies are without exception restricted to an analysis of phenomena with a view to discovering their laws, meaning constant relations of sequences or similarity. They can never be concerned with the inner nature of the phenomena, their effective or final causes or their essential mode of production.' Without formally denouncing the use of the term 'cause' Comte re-introduced into the thought of the 19th century the distinction between laws and causes without giving to laws any particular dignity. Laws were in, causes were out. The value of theories is reduced to the function of anticipating the results of experiments. To take theory seriously can only lead to chimeric conceptions. Hence, no unification of different parts of physics such as electricity and optics can be expected, beyond the formal use of similar mathematical techniques.

Brunschvicg has pointed out that while Comte was producing his ideas, developments were taking place in physics contrary to those which Comte indicated. A concept of energy was growing up which tied the theory of heat to mechanics. Mayer, Colding and Joule established in 1842 the equivalence of work and heat - the law of conservation of energy: 'If a quantity of heat is gained or dissipated in a process, an amount of work is lost or produced which is related to the former by a universal factor.' Energy - the term was proposed by Young in 1807 but popularised only much later by Lord Kelvin - appeared as a universal substance capable of Protean transformations; it was at times almost sanctified as the basic reality which was behind the old idea that the cause equals the effect. After the thermal, the magnetic and electric phenomena were found to be subject to the law of conservation of energy, and optics became a chapter of electrodynamics. Quite generally, the division of physics into doctrines ceased to be a fundamental issue.

Maine de Biran's (1766-1824) reaction to Hume was opposite to that of Comte's.

Hume could find no rational or external foundation for the belief in causality. This Biran accepted: but the conclusion he drew from this was not Hume's. It was that we must search elsewhere for the foundation of causality. In general, Biran argued, the evidence required for a proposition depends on its type: for the rule of causality we require immediate evidence, which means for Biran psychological, spiritual or, in the last resort, metaphysical evidence. He traced the origin of causality to the sensations accompanying our efforts.

Neither the perception of external objects nor mathematical ideas provide the evidence required because the primary fact is not a sensation but the consciousness of it. Descartes' mistake was to take it as primarily evident that consciousness and extension are separate substances, whereas in fact our first impressions are that 'I act', 'I carry out a voluntary action, hence I cause' - where the 'I' does not represent an impersonal consciousness but the personal 'I'. This makes the cause-effect relation the primary way in which we approach the world - no wonder therefore that we cannot deny it or 'establish' it independently.

The 'I' *(ego, moi)* begins to exist for itself only by the exercise of free activity, i.e. in the conscious effort which is coupled with a particular sensation, *sui generis,* tied to this effort as is effect to its cause. Also the 'I' exhausts itself totally and indivisibly in this relation of a cause which acts to the effect which is produced. The cause is felt or perceived in the effort which itself is perceived by the muscular sensation to which it leads. This relation between action on the one hand and changes in exterior objects on the other, which we experience as cause and effect, could not be conceived if there did not exist objectively or absolutely a similar relation between the two substances or forces. If the physicists pride themselves on having reduced their science to experimentally observed relations between phenomena, they pride themselves on an impossible victory. To disallow causality, they would have to disallow the thinking 'I' whilst continuing to think and to reason. Biran admits however, elsewhere in his essays that causes in nature are occult and that scientific explanations consist essentially of the analysis of experimental conditions. But psychology, even experimental psychology, cannot, according to Biran, operate sensibly without the full recognition of the cause-effect relationships.

J.S. Mill (1806-1873). The development of the experimental sciences had greatly accelerated after Hume's time, and was largely the outcome of a determined search for causes. It was this which suggested to John Stuart Mill that there is more to causality than Hume's association of ideas.

Mill was convinced that a new inductive logic could establish causality. He realised that induction is not merely a collection of case-histories, that it could be based on even a single case and he concluded that it should be founded on the dissection into its elementary sequences and uniformities of the intricate web and aggregation of observed nature. Each sequence obeys its own law; it has been shown to be futile to search for the one law of nature. 'The universality of the law of causation consists in each particular consequent being tied to a particular antecedent, or a group of particular antecedents'. 'The cause, philosophically speaking, is the sum of positive and negative conditions, taking together the total of all contingencies of nature which, when present, make the consequent invariably follow'. For this, 'we have no ulterior test to which we subject experience in general but we make experience its own test'. That means that the 'law of causality' itself is an inductive final generalisation of a multitude of phenomena of partial or particular uniformities of succession, so that it has a foundation which is, however, no stronger than the particular sequences from which it is derived. Of course, some primitive experiences such as that living creatures need nourishment, fire burns, and water drowns, are not open to doubt. Mill realised that the popular usage of 'cause' singles out now this, now that condition as the cause.

Mill failed to see that the significance of assigning a cause consists precisely in this singling out. Therefore, he based the scientific use of the law of causality on the analysis of complicated situations into large sets of antecedents ABCD and sets of consequents a b c d, which have to be disentangled. To this Brunschvicg has pointed out that the actual scientific situations are not given in terms of threads ABCD, abcd. Mill himself mentions that the ways of nature never at first glance show anything but 'chaos upon chaos'. This may be a strong statement, but an easily recognised antecedent need not be the cause. Bright starlight for instance often precedes heavy dew without causing it; the soil cools rapidly when the sky is clear.

It may be even more to the point to query the whole underlying model, viz. that of a web, tissue or felt. For a tissue or felt consists of individual fibres, though they may be interlocked. But the nature we live in and that is described by Mill does not consist of strands of one kind, but has colours and atoms, sentiments and sounds, hot and cold and love and hatred .... i.e. it consists of elements of very different kinds. After having taken a tissue to pieces, you can weigh the pieces and satisfy yourself that you have accounted for the lot. Nothing of this kind can be done with the elements of nature which cannot be counted and added up, until you have reduced them to atoms and elementary particles. That, however, was not Mill's idea.

Schopenhauer (1788-1860) made some interesting points, mainly following Aristotle, although he preferred to see himself associated with Plato and Kant. His ideas were first presented in his Ph.D. Thesis (presented at Jena, like that of Karl Marx) entitled 'On the fourfold root of the principle of sufficient reason'.

The principle of sufficient reason is, according to Schopenhauer, the basis of all science. It has rightly been formulated as *one* principle: *Nihil est sine ratione cur potius sit, quam non sit.* 'Nothing is without a reason why it should be rather than not be'. Our consciousness is divided into subject and object and all objects are objects for the subject, or ideas. All ideas are connected in a law-like and formally *a priori* determined manner, so that nothing isolated can become an object. Hence the principle of sufficient reason. It has four different roots, as there are four classes of objects. We have

(a) real objects of perception where the principle takes the form of the relation between cause and effect controlling the succession of changes. Both cause and effect are always individual changes and the chain of changes has no beginning and no end. The substances, i.e. material bodies, carry the changes, or in them the changes take place. The laws of conservation of matter and the law of inertia are therefore corollaries to the principle of cause and effect. Natural forces as general ideas provide the rules according to which, or through which, individual changes take place. Rules and individual changes must not be equated, as Maine de Biran did. Schopenhauer claims special credit for discriminating between the two concepts. In fact these were sometimes but not always confused, (for instance not by Burgersdijk who separates causes of particular events from causes in general).

(b) The second class of objects consists of concepts and propositions which are connected as premises and conclusions. To this applies the *logical* norm of sufficient reason which, even after Kant, has been confused with the physical law of cause and effect. Schopenhauer considers this confusion particularly obnoxious.

(c) A third class of object is provided by mathematics. In geometry, for instance, neither are we concerned with sequences in time nor is the connection between geometrical objects purely logical. Yet we still have a determined sequence of notions.

(d) The fourth class is concerned with motivation. The subject recognizes itself only as subject of 'volition', that is a willing, desiring subject; it cannot double itself up and see itself as subject of 'cognition', that is as knowing, observing subject. Volition is always fully motivated. The law of motivation is the principle of sufficient reason of action. Motivation is so to speak causality seen from inside. There is no place left for a freedom of will; if there is a conflict of motivations, the strongest motive will win.

Brunschvicg (1869-1944). The problems which philosophers from the 16th to the 19th century saw in causality were critically reviewed and analysed by Leon Brunschvicg (1922) in a remarkable book, *L'experience humaine et la causalité physique.*

Brunschvicg takes the ideas and applications of the principle of causality as belonging to a continuing dialogue between man and nature. It is only by way of abstraction that the phenomena of the universe appear as independent from the mind which knows them, so that the problem of causality is not so much a problem of a philosophy of nature or of a philosophy of science as of the philolophy of thought and history. Brunschvicg is a follower of Kant, but he criticises Kant for being too schematic and too static; Kant's philosophy must be revised in the light of non-Euclidean geometry and the theory of relativity. Nature is not presented to man as a gift; there is no such thing as immediate experience of objects: they are constituted by the causal nexus. The best enunciation of the function of causality would be the proposition that a universe exists. Causality should therefore not be described in anthropomorphic terms such as to associate efficacy (productive activity) with it. Kant's antinomy disappears when proper attention is given to the condition by which the idea of causality arises, and how causality constitutes the object. For it is a succession of past events which provides the basis for determinism. Even astronomical forecasts refer to laws persisting from the past; but the past contains historical facts which have no explanation but the confluence of independent causes. Hence, concludes Brunschvicg, the extrapolation of determinism to the future is not justified: the process of time transforms what was contingent into necessity.

One philosopher of the first half of the 19th century and his school Brunschvicg scathingly denounced as having excluded themselves in a reactionary manner from the dialogue with nature: *Hegel (1770-1831)* and his followers, *Marx (1818-1883)* and *Engels (1820-1895).*

Brunschvicg writes about Hegel: 'It had to become necessary to accept a status of philosophy ..... which would appear as subordinated to knowledge .... This was not Hegel's point of view. He detached himself from contemporary science as having become too complex, too devious, too unstable to serve the interest of a dogmatic speculation which requires simple and definite systems. In consequence, he had to fall back on the disused tackle of a rudimentary and outdated scholastic.'

Against this it may be stated not only that Hegel is still widely studied, but also that the theory of becoming, which is here of interest, has, slightly modified by Marx and Engels, become the creed of every large community. To the ways of becoming discussed above, Hegel added the dialectic process.

'Hegel understands by what he called dialectic. (i) a property of all our thoughts, in virtue of which each particular thought necessarily passes over into another, but also (ii) a property of things in virtue of which every particular thing necessarily belongs together with all other things ..... since every concept is limited, it passes over, when logically thought out, into its opposite, its negation. To think it out is to annul it. But through the negation there arises a new positive ... negation means that a new concept comes into force .... which is richer than the latter .... The system of concepts has to form itself and to complete itself in a ceaseless, pure progression - free from any accretion from without.' (Höffding (1900) Vol. II,180)

The decisive point is that Hegel takes this logical dialectic as an expression of the self-development of historical and natural objects. Hence, it should be possible - so his critics objected - to derive history and science by pure thought and to arrive at total knowledge very much more easily than Laplace's intelligence could have done it. As a matter of fact, however, the triad position, - negation, - higher unity, indicated by the dialectic, is only a schema into which Hegel fits empirical content.

Taking over from Hegel the idea that becoming is governed by a dialectical process rather than by a cause-effect relation, but disregarding Hegel's logical and spiritual basis, *Marx* and *Engels* put forward the idea of dialectical materialism.

Materialism teaches that the world is in the first instance matter - anything that is not describable as matter is only disguised matter or property of matter. There was a universe before there was anyone to think about it. Dialectical materialism differs from simple materialism in three respects:

(a) matter is not just taken as atoms or rocks or bones, but includes economic conditions of human societies as distinct from spiritual or religious conventions:

(b) it does not take objects as given but as having their significance only in connection with their part in the process of evolution;

(c) and this process of evolution occurs by a dialectic development. Developments and changes always take place, often slowly and barely noticeably. In time however such small changes build up until they create conditions which are incompatible with the situation in which the development took place and hence lead to the overthrow of this situation and the creation of a new one: the thesis, the old situation, has generated the antithesis and, by qualitative change, a new synthesis. In this way novelty comes into being, galaxies and stars, life on earth, evolution, mankind, social life, ... feudal society, capitalism and communism. 'It is from the history of nature and human society that the laws of dialectics are abstracted. For they are nothing but the most general laws of these two aspects of historical development, as well as of thought itself. They can be reduced in the main to three:

the law of transformation of quantity into quality and vice versa;

the law of the interpenetration of opposites;

the law of the negation of the negations (Engels)

A simple physical example of transformation of quantity into quality is a change from ice into water, from a rigid crystalline body into an amorphous fluid. The gradual addition of heat to ice has no qualitative effect until at a specific point crystallinity and regularity disappear suddenly to be replaced by the fluidity of water. It is not claimed that the dialectical process can always be observed, and on any scale; changes become dialectically understandable only when a large process is considered as a whole. It cannot for example normally be applied to the material which a scientist handles, but must be applied to the scientist and his material at the same time, including the general technical, social and economic conditions of the country he is working in. Marx saw dialectical materialism particularly verified in the economic and political development of capitalism: exploitation for profit leads to a form of production, distribution and political control, all of which are susceptible to gradual change, but through all these changes it creates conditions such as monopolies which are the antithesis of competitive capitalism and eventually must lead to revolutionary change, the negation of the negation, viz. the replacement of the capitalistic by a communistic regime.

Advocates of dialectical materialism point out that the modern physical world picture is full of antitheses and opposites and is a standing example of the failure of the older logic; in particular, they point at particles and waves as opposite concepts neither of which alone is able to interpret all properties of radiation and electrons.

That, however, dialectical materialism will not likely be in competition with the older ideas of necessity and chance can be seen from the following passages quoted from an article by J.D. Bernal (1934), a scientist who is a partisan of dialectical materialism.

Bernal considers mechanical materialism as a 'mythological' abstraction. 'Scientific knowledge uses in any field a set of entities differing in quality, in their laws of combination, from those used in other fields'. The world is always changing: 'The central idea in dialectical materialism is that of transformation. The two-sided problem is: how do transformations occur and how can we make transformations occur. The approach to this problem lies in an examination of all observable facts .... dialectical materialism .... is concerned primarily with the new.'

'The unity of opposites and the change from quantity into quality are .... universal modes of behaviour ... but that does not mean that it would be possible to demonstrate the dialectic process in any small portion of the field of nature or humanity. To apply the dialectic to the material, whether inorganic or biological, in the hands of a scientist is simply to make nonsense of it. The dialectic must be applied to the scientist and his material at one time. The application of dialectics to experimental science is much more its application to the history of science and the directions of fruitful future scientific fields of discovery than it is to the actual description and deductions from concrete experiment.'

'Until the Russian revolution, Marxism had practically no effect on the course of the physical sciences, yet the history of the physical sciences in the 19th and the 20th centuries shows a steady drift away from the simple mechanical views of Newton ·

into a set of irreducible dialectical opposites such as waves and particles, matter and energy ... from the dialectical point of view there is nothing illogical in any of these pairs of united opposites.'

5
The Renaissance of Chance

The philosophers of the early 19th century did not, as the preceding review has shown, consider chance a worthwhile object of thought. This changed towards the end of the century.

There was *Windelband (1848-1918)* in Germany who published a small book under the title *The Theories of Chance (Die Lehren vom Zufall, 1870)*. Windelband's view of chance is that expected from a parson towards sin; he must take note of it but is against it.

After explaining that the concept of the contingent or accidental has its root in the idea of the possible, Windelband, following Hegel, defines the contingent as the possible which has become a fact without necessity - an event that could have been different. 'Necessary' means following from the preceding situation according to a rigorous law. How and why the law acts remains a riddle as we have no *intimate* understanding of the cause-effect relation.

Chance is incompatible with efficient causes; the law that every change has its causes by which it is necessarily brought about, is generally recognised as the basis of all science and all thought. Human consciousness provides no exception, cause takes here the form of motives. Motives are a form of causes effective in men and hence in history; they determine the future with no less certainty than mechanical causes do in the mechanical world. The historical sciences differ from the natural sciences by the interest they take in particular single events, but history is governed no less by necessity than is the mechanical world. One still finds widespread the assumption of a freedom of choice and hence, says Windelband, a suspension of the law of motivation, but the progress of psychology leads to psychological determinism. The causal activity of consciousness gives the impression of freedom, although it follows rigorous laws. Freedom is the ability to recognise the motives which influence the will according to the particular nature of the individual; freedom means also obedience to norm; unfree is he who blindly follows passion. However, says Windelband, the certainty of causation does not deprive us of moral responsibility which would even be impossible without causality. For responsibility rests on a different plane.

We believe we experience accidental events if our knowledge of the conditions is deficient; Windelband quotes Hume: 'Though there be no such thing as chance in the world, our ignorance of the real cause of any event has the same influence on the understanding and begets a like species of belief or opinion'. We are, for instance, often ignorant of the origins of two chains of sequences which come together; such a coincidence is not true chance, for the sequences can have a common cause or a common origin in the distant past.

It may now be argued that the scientific explanation through efficient causes is not the final principle of reason, which asks for purposes and final causes. The concept of purpose is not necessarily in conflict with that of cause and necessity, and the notion of an accidentally achieved purpose is different from that of an accidental effect. But we may also look for purposes outside our own activity. Human ignorance may mistake divine purpose for chance or a two-chain coincidence for divine purpose. Also, let us look at the world as a whole: if a causal mechanism as such is to have value, it must realise a purpose and should itself not be taken as contingent.

Finally, logical analysis separates the essential from the inessential which is then taken as accidental; but reality is complete and the separation of essential and inessential or accidental arises only in the abstraction. Here too, it is only the limitation of the human mind which suggests the occurrence of chance. Windelband concludes that chance is thought of only where the general and the particular are torn apart in the mind; we should rely on all scientific, moral and artistic life to carry on a persistent and in the end victorious fight against the belief in chance. Windelband was penetrating enough to be challenged by the problem of chance, but his discussion remains rather superficial.

Simmel, (1848-1915) a more subtle thinker, was, like Windelband, impressed by the progress of historical studies. In the *Problems of the philosophy of history (Die Probleme der Geschichtsphilosophie, 1892),* he begins by reminding the reader of the fragmentary character of our Weltbild.

We are inclined to gloss over vital gaps. This applies in particular to our appreciation of historical developments. In history many causes with many facets co-operate: more causes than can be incorporated in a comprehensible description. This makes it difficult to trace elementary cause-effect sequences which alone can be expected to follow general laws.

But it is not even logically necessary, suggests Simmel, to identify causality and unique sequences. A could on one occasion causally produce B and on another occasion C, and as there is no logical hindrance in the connection AB or AC, there can be none in connecting A with either B or C. Such ambiguous connection which may be called individual causality has still all the marks of causality without requiring a cause for the deviation. It may well exist and be the root of the freedom of the soul.

It is truly remarkable how close Simmel, being a student of the arts rather than of the sciences, comes here to describing the situation with which physicists are faced now, and it is not astounding that after having proposed his idea, Simmel almost at once withdraws it because he considers it infertile. In practice, he thought, such an ambiguous or many-valued causality could not be tested and distinguished from a mere sequence. Nor was this idea of individual causality appreciated by contemporary authors such as *Rickert,* who also wrote about the philosophy of history. The historian's interest is, he claims, centred on the individual event whereas the scientist's interest is centred on the laws. Nevertheless, rigorous univalued laws must be assumed to control the objects of the sciences.

Simmel's idea of 'individual' causality was, probably independently, put forward again by Silberstein in 1933. Silberstein suggested the name polyfurcation for this situation; but having thought about it and described it, he did not become more assertive about it than did Simmel. Even in 1933, the message of chance had not come home yet. A better term for the situation here envisaged would perhaps be *'forked'* causality.

But a kind of advocacy of chance has also persisted through the 19th century. Perhaps more thought was given to chance, on and off, than we are aware, but it was swept under the carpet as unpopular and unsuccessful. There is an article *The Seven Questions,* written in 1886 by the remarkable physiologist, *E. Du Bois-*

Reymond (1818-1896). Du Bois-Reymond first restates very nicely Epicurus' case, without referring to him.

'If notions and volitions are simply necessary and single-valued accessories of movements of molecules in the brain, no freedom of the will can exist'. He then reminds the reader of the peculiar classical example of free will, Buridan's ass, who is not expected to starve in spite of being placed between two equally attractive bundles of hay. The situation between the bundles of hay requires a decision of free will; physically it corresponds to a neutral point in mechanics which could therefore be studied as a physical analogue of free will. Now according to Du Bois-Reymond, such studies had in fact been carried out by *Cournet* in Dijon, *Boussenesque* in Lille and *de Saint Venant* in Paris. As an example, consider a geometrical hill and a rolling ball. There exists a singular solution - when the ball comes to rest on top of the hill from which it can be moved with infinitely small mechanical energy in any direction. Du Bois-Reymond does not consider this attempt as very significant because he thinks the displacement would require an energy of activation.

We would disregard these examples because they are not on the atomic scale but I think it is satisfactory to learn that such attempts have been made.

Then, towards the end of the century, a new group of philosophers came to the foreground in America who took chance seriously, before the development of physics made chance a topic of special interest. James, Peirce and Dewey re-considered the place of chance in world affairs.

Determinism pleads, according to *James, (1842-1910)* that those parts of the universe already laid down absolutely appoint and decree what the other parts shall be. Against this, indeterminism suggests that parts have a certain amount of loose play one about another; that there are possibilities in excess of actualities. There exists a certain ultimate pluralism - there are possibilities everywhere, but not necessity. Chance is not just crazy unreason, it is, however, a purely selective and negative term stating that the object is disconnected from something else. The system of other things has no hold on the chance-thing, in which there is something of its own. Now the only ambiguous things we are tempted to believe in are future human volitions. If somebody has the choice of walking home alternative equivalent ways, neither way can be said to be impossible, or to be the rational or necessary one either. To say the choice is predetermined doesn't help in any way. The ' accident' of choice is not absolute, for home he will walk; all the futures that offer themselves to our choice spring equally from the soil of the past. Internally, the acts of choice are self-luminous decisions.

Apart from the difficulty that strictly speaking our judgements themselves would be necessitated, determinism leads to a dilemma in the light of the incurable taint with which the universe is coloured. Either we succumb to a fatalistic pessimism or we smooth over consciences by calling all cruelty and sorrows good, as contrivances for deepening the theoretical consciousness of what goodness and evil in their intrinsic nature are. This is a subjectivistic point of view. It ends with the most corrupt curiosity and spiritual, moral and practical licence. Against this James appeals for conduct, not sensibility, to be the ultimate fact for our recognition. The essence of the philosophy of objective conduct is the recognition of limits foreign and opaque to our understanding. The universe belongs to a plurality of semi-independent forces, and the only consistent way of representing a pluralism is the indeterministic one: better the chance of a good world than a world without chance.

Charles S. Peirce (1839-1914) was an even more staunch advocate of chance:

the world contains chance as one of its pervasive features. It is not a mere illusion provoked by our ignorance. Irreversible heat transfer in physics, psychological observation and moral choice and responsibility point against necessity.

What, after all, are the reasons for the proposition that the state of things existing at any time, together with certain immutable laws, completely determines the state of things, including minds, at every other time? Is it a postulate? A postulate is a provisional inference, but all essential inferences are from sampling, which is subject to fluctuations. There are continuous quantities which are assumed to have exact values, but this is not founded on the experimenter's observation. Thirdly, while there is regularity in nature, this regularity is not exact. Finally, it has been claimed that chance has not been found to produce signal effects. Against this claim one can point to kinetic theory and entropy. It must therefore be concluded that precise and universal conformity of facts to law is not clearly proved or even made probable; chance is neither inconceivable nor unintelligible.

Peirce analysed the process of experimental observation and concluded that chance is not an illusion arising merely from our ignorance, but an irreducible factor in physical processes and hence an ultimate category for the existential universe. The most convincing evidence for the relevance of chance in the universe comes from the development of life. Whilst the number of elementary degrees of freedom remains constant, history shows growth and increasing complexity. Why should all specifications go back to the beginning of things? Spontaneity of life is not accounted for by mechanical laws. The necessitarians do not account for the diversity and irregularity of the universe. 'I attribute the whole specification of the world .... altogether to chance, in the form of a spontaneity which is to some degree regular'. With all this Peirce did not deny necessity or laws of nature, but he only wanted their limits to be recognised. Gravitation may be a law of nature and if the followers of Hume deny this necessity of gravitation - meaning that each event which gravitation formulates is independent of every other - they make the universe utterly unintelligible. Laws of nature, or sometimes its customs, are found by conjecture and checked or pinned down by experience, but neither the laws nor the customs of nature are all-pervasive.

John Dewey, (1859-1952) living well into the age of quantum problems, derived his inspiration like James and Peirce from human existence rather than from the progress of science. The path from human existence to science is a theme of Dewey's *Experience and Nature, 1929.*

Man finds himself, Dewey writes, living in an 'aleatory' world (dependent on the throw of a die). His existence involves, to put it boldly, a gamble. The world is a scene of risk; it is uncertain and uncannily unstable. Our magical safeguard against the uncertain character of the world is to deny the existence of chance, to mumble about universal and necessary law, the ubiquity of cause and effect, the uniformity of nature, universal progress and the inherent rationality of the universe. The safeguard comes from our own labour. From the point of view of labour a thing is what it will do to other things. Extraordinary and subtle reasons have been assigned for believing in the principle of causation. Labour and the use of tools seem, however, to be sufficient empirical reasons; indeed, to be the only empirical events that can be specifically pointed to in this connection ... more adequate than regular sequences or categories of reason or the alleged fact of will. Labour and the use of tools imply causality as the sequential order itself, both as initiation and finality or efficient and final causation; a cause is that antecedent which if manipulated regulates the occurrence of the consequent.

So the ultimate objects of science are guided processes of change; science seizes upon what is sufficiently uniform to make the changes of nature predictable. If only uniformity existed, thought and knowledge would be impossible and needless. Only the incomplete and uncertain gives point and application to ascertainment of regular relations and orders. Frustration experienced in this process is interpreted according to the prevailing culture: in Europe as due to the opposed existences of object and subject as independent forms of being. Objects are not immediately *had;* objects are whatever we are aware of, are events *with* meaning: tables, the milky way, cats, electrons, historical epochs. The question of stimuli is a question of existential causation; it refers to something extrinsic to be reached by enquiry and inference. The consciousness of stimuli marks the conclusion of an investigation, not an original datum. It is impossible to deduce consciousness from physical laws.

Science does not grasp reality in its final self-sufficient form; discovery is not a treasure hunt but it creates transformation of both the meanings and the existence of nature. It is impossible to tell what immediate consciousness or immediate qualities such as sweet or red are ... they are something *had,* not communicated or known. According to the now traditional view, the object of knowledge is reality *par excellence,* the immediate qualities gathered together into a psychic realm of being; but reality is more than a double-barrelled word - the most dangerous of all philosophical words. One mode of experience should not be separated from other modes and their things.

Once it is recognised that the mathematico-mechanical world does not have an existence independent of love, appreciation and devotion, that the proper object of knowledge has the character appropriate to the subject matter of the useful arts - problems such as freedom and the relation of the physical and the mental evaporate.

The individual analyses and interprets experience and nature in terms of the conclusions of the natural sciences which themselves are based on experience and nature. This is the existential and historical circularity. It is part of the evolution of man - not an unfolding of what was previously latent but an actualisation of potentialities through interactions not known beforehand. As an individual response cannot be predicted but after the event is linked with its sources, so the path of an individual electron cannot be calculated. The principle of indeterminacy is thus a generalisation of the idea that the individual has a temporal career whose future cannot be logically deduced from the past.

6

Decline and Fall of Physical Necessity

The progress of the sciences in the 19th century at first confirmed scientists in the strict determinism to which they had been conditioned.

There were the triumphs of Newtonian dynamics. In 1821, Alexis Bouvard computed new tables of Uranus, with a view to allowing for more recent observations. However, he could not eradicate the discrepancies between the observed and computed places for the planet. Was Newton's law of gravitation at fault? Or was the disturbance due to an unknown planet? In October 1845, John Couch Adams, a young Cambridge mathematician, estimated the orbit of the hypothetical perturbing planet and communicated the elements of its orbit to the Astronomer Royal - who was sceptical. One year later Le Verrier independently proved that the irregularities of the motion of Uranus could not be due to any known planet, and subsequently calculated the elements of the orbit of this hypothetical body, and its probable position. In September 1846 he wrote about it to Professor Galle of the Berlin Observatory who, within 48 hours found the missing planet, Neptune.

Electric and magnetic phenomena came more and more under control. The idea of 'fields', such as electric fields, i.e. continuous distributions of properties in space, governed by laws capable of being formulated with no less precision than those which applied to Newtonian particles, had become familiar. Atomism had gained new stature through the determination of Avogadro's number, the number of atoms in a unit weight of matter. Atoms had ceased to be just very small and had become objects of definite research. Early in the 19th century they were found to be capable of carrying electric charges. Towards the end of the century it was discovered that these could be detached by light from metallic surfaces (the photo-electric effect). In evacuated tubes the electric charges appeared as cathode rays, consisting of small particles which were called electrons. The enquiry into causes had been successful everywhere and made physics and chemistry technologically productive. New industries were developing in the wake of the progress of electrical knowledge, providing additional evidence of the validity of the basic assumptions.

But by and by in the 19th century cases and fields of study came under consideration in which laws and causes appeared to be replaced by randomness and chance.

Randomness is popularly obtained by throwing dice or tossing a coin. In the first instance, it defines not the structure of the result, but the way it comes about. The result can, however, indicate the random origin. The result, for instance of tossing a coin, is a sequence of digits one and nought, if one denotes heads and nought denotes tails. The randomness of the sequence could be recognised by the impossibility of describing it in any shorter way than by reciting it in full, whereas an orderly sequence such as 0 1 0 1 0 1 .... can be given by a simple rule. This criterion was independently proposed in 1965 by A.N. Kolmogorov and G.J. Chaitin (Chaitin, 1975). Any poet or author would claim of his work precisely the same, that its content could not be fully conveyed except by reciting it, implying that the letters form a mathematically random sequence. What a vindication of Epicurus' postulate!

In a random sequence it is not possible to tell how far you are from the beginning; any portion of a given length should have approximately the same average value wherever it is picked: the average should neither systematically increase nor decrease.

It was already at the end of the 18th century confirmed by *Count Rumford (1753-1814)* that heat is not a fluid added to a body but a movement of its constituents. Experiment had shown that there is no limit to the amount of heat which can be produced by rubbing together two pieces of metal. In gases this motion of the constituent molecules takes the form of their free translation, interrupted only by collisions with each other and the walls of the container. It suffices here to visualize the molecules as elastic balls. The model explains at once why gases have no shape or volume. They exert pressure on the walls, the pressure which drives our motor cars; the impact of a molecule on the wall is not normally individually observable but the average effect of millions of impacts is observed as a steady pressure. It could be thought that in order to calculate this pressure, and other properties of gases such as thermal conduction and diffusion, it is only necessary to write down the equations of motion of the molecules, take some initial condition and to see what effect the collisions have on the velocities and positions. Unfortunately this procedure is not feasible because the number of molecules even in a small volume is too large. The age of the earth is short compared with the time required to carry out this programme.

The only way of dealing with the properties of gases was therefore to treat them as averages of random events. Data such as the average speed of the molecules, depending on the temperature of the gas, their mass and size, were found sufficient to build up the kinetic theory of gases, and eventually statistical mechanics, theories which account quantitatively for the properties of gases and other systems, including such irregular deviations from normal behaviour as must occur in random assemblies.

Now, this incursion of chance seemed a matter of convenience rather than of principle, and many attempts were made to prove that the collision of molecules must according to Newtonian dynamics rapidly lead to all configurations which could exist if these were generated at random. These attempts did not meet with success but the failure was regarded as a technical hitch rather than evidence of chance as a primary fact.

A more serious, but also more obscure challenge to causality was offered by *Balmer's (1825-1898)* discovery of the law of the hydrogen spectrum (1885). Newton using a glass prism had shown that white light consisted of differently refrangible rays. In 1752 Melville observed that a sodium flame emits pure yellow light. The construction of the spectroscope by *Fraunhofer (1787-1826)* led to the study of the spectra of flames, electric arcs, the sun and the stars and electric discharges in rarefied gases. In 1859 Kirchhoff and Bunsen outlined the principles of chemical analysis by spectral methods; they showed that under given conditions each element emits a well-defined line spectrum, i.e. light which is deflected by the prism through a set of sharply defined angles; the angle of deflection is for any particular prism a simple function of the wavelength of the light. The spectrum is characteristic of the emitting element. But attempts to find a formula which connected the different wavelengths emitted by an element were not successful until Balmer was able to show that the lines of the hydrogen spectrum obey with great precision the formula

$$\lambda = R \frac{m^2}{m^2 - 4}$$

where R is a constant and m has integer values 3,4,5.... Classical physics could account for systems capable of emitting light at one fixed wavelength or perhaps even of several wavelengths but not for a set connected by a rule given by a formula like Balmer's. Similar rules were soon found to apply to other elements; even so the outrageous form of the rules failed to shake confidence in the foundations of physics such as were known at that time.

Radioactivity - the mysterious radiation emitted by some minerals - was discovered by *H. Becquerel (1852-1908)* and radium by *Marie (1867-1934)* and *Pierre (1851-1906) Curie* in 1898. In the next few years a host of other radioactive elements were isolated and studied. Some of them were found to decay rapidly after they had been isolated, i.e. the specimen ceased rapidly to be active. In 1901 P. and M. Curie, H. Becquerel and J. Perrin put forward the view that radioactivity was an atomic transformation process, as it was frequently observed that a new activity appeared as the original one decayed. In 1902 *Rutherford (1871-1937)* and *Soddy* established the law of exponential decay, which implies that the activity is proportional to the amount of active matter left. This could only mean that either the radioactive matter emits radiation steadily until it disappears or that each atom relieves itself at a particular instant of a definite amount of surplus energy. In 1903 Crookes, and Elster and Geitel observed brief and highly localised unpredictable bursts of light (scintillations) on fluorescent screens placed near a radium source, at points where emitted particles could strike the screen. This was the first time in history that an effect due to a single atom was observed. The flashes were found to be caused by alpha particles. This proved finally that the activity is not a continuous process, and Rutherford and Soddy concluded that radiation is emitted by an atom as it undergoes a transmutation from one elementary form into another. What then causes a transmutation? It was found that their rate could not be influenced by any manipulation. No causal explanation was ever found which explained the instant of the transmutation. The more that became known about radioactivity, the more likely did it become that the date of a disintegration was a matter of pure chance. Ten years later C.T.R. Wilson invented the 'cloud chamber' which made it possible to study the tracks in a gas· of single particles emitted in the process of disintegration; but you never know when the tracks will appear. The particles are of two kinds: alpha particles are positively charged helium atoms; beta particles are electrons, known from gas discharges, which carry a negative charge; their mass is about 1/7000 that of the helium atoms. Gamma rays are a third kind of radiation emitted by radioactive nuclei. Gamma rays are electromagnetic radiation like light, radio waves or X-rays, carry no charge and leave no tracks in their passage through gases. In 1911 Rutherford used alpha particles to probe other atoms with the result that the space occupied by an atom turned out to be mainly empty. Within that space there is a nucleus with linear dimensions about 1/100,000 of that of the atom and a number of electrons of similar size.

The nuclei are responsible for the radioactivity. Each kind of radioactive nucleus has a characteristic lifetime, which is simply related to the probability of its decaying in a given interval of time. If this was, e.g. 1/100th for an interval of one second, and we have 100,000 atoms, then approximately 1000 will decay during the next second.

Poor Democritus! The pursuit of the very studies he had initiated had now led to a gross contradiction of his idea of necessity and of the indivisible atom. If an atom can spit out some of its matter and change as a result it is obviously no longer indivisible. How right was Aristotle to query the concept of the indivisibility of a geometrically extended body!

Today we reconcile the two views through the concept of the effort required to cause breaks in the elementary unit. Assume for a moment that diamonds were as ubiquitous as gravel; they would be used as such, being particularly lasting. If it is then discovered that they can be burnt in specially constructed furnaces, that would add to their usefulness without in any way interfering with the former use because the new way of handling the material is not related to their use as gravel: the forces involved in the two processes are too different.

Radioactivity needed discovering because it is an exception. Atoms in the normal chemical sense are indeed indivisible and indestructible, as Demoncritus had postulated. In ordinary physical analysis atoms remain Democritean. The discovery of natural radioactivity showed that some nuclei are in fact not indivisible, but tend to break up of their own accord. The later discovery of artificial radioactivity led to the conclusion that all nuclei consist of protons (nuclei of hydrogen atoms) and neutrons (which are protons less their electrical charge) but this does not affect their stability under ordinary conditions.

With regard to the question of necessity and chance it is irrelevant that Democritean atoms are not the ultimate units from which the world is built. What is relevant to these questions is not the indivisibility of atoms but the simplicity of forces.

The decisive step in the evolution of the new physics, which gave rise to the appellation classical physics for the earlier science, was, of course, *Planck's (1858-1947)* introduction of quanta of energy. Planck was not encouraged in his studies. As he recounts in a short autobiographical note, he was warned by Professor W. Jolly that physics was an 'almost fully mature science... Perhaps one could find in a corner, or in a niche, a spot of dust or a little bubble worth examining, but the system was well established.' Planck did not set out to produce a theory of those effects which resisted interpretation by causal laws. The little bubble which Planck studied was, put into common language, the colour of the light of a candle. Kirchhoff had shown that the spectral distribution, i.e. the colour and brightness of the light emitted by hot 'black', and practically all hot bodies, depend only on their temperature. Hence, argued Planck, it must be possible to find and to derive from first principles a universal law which governs the emission of that light. The problem turned out to be obstinate. But eventually, in 1900, Planck arrived at a promising formula which implied the existence of an elementary quantum of action - Planck's constant h. Such a constant could not be fitted into the framework of known physics. 'It revealed', said Planck in 1920 in his Nobel Prize address, 'something absolutely new, something unheard of, which seemed to be destined to revolutionise our ideas of physics which, since the foundation of the differential calculus by Leibniz and Newton, were based upon the assumption of the continuity of all causal relations.' The existence of the constant means that changes of energy cannot take place in arbitrarily small units, but only in definite amounts, just as you can pay for purchases only in integral multiples of the smallest coin in circulation. The analogy with the unprovoked decay of radioactive atoms is obvious. Planck's quantum theory was not a hypothesis but the inescapable result of a rigorous analysis of facts. Planck could not find any cause for the stepped release of light, just as Newton could find none for gravitation.

As the years went by, the concept of quanta illuminated an increasing number of known phenomena and provoked the discovery of a new range of physical effects which could not be interpreted on a deterministic basis.

There was the photo-electric effect. In order to appreciate its significance, let us remember how firmly the wave theory of light was grounded. The strongest evidence had come from a host of interference experiments. In a variety of ways the light issuing from a source can be split into two or more parts and then reunited. Where the rays come together, a pattern appears of bright and dark patches, the bright region being brighter and the dark region being darker than they would be if illuminated by one portion only of the emitted light. This is because waves have 'phases', in addition to strength; as a result, two portions combined can produce less effect than one alone - in the way 1 combined with 1 can be 0 or two according to the sign of the combination.

The photo-electric effect was discovered by Hertz in 1897; it was further studied by Hallwachs, Elster and Geitel, and others. Electrons are constituents of atoms but can be detached from them and formed into rays. They excite the screens of our television picture tubes; but such application was still below the horizon. The 1897 discovery was that electrons could be detached from metallic surfaces simply by illumination. Then, in 1902 Lenard found that the initial speed of the emitted electrons is independent of the intensity of the light which produces the effect and depends solely on its colour. Now, each electron comes from a particular atom, a tiny spot somewhere on the surface, so small that a thousand million million (10^{15}) spots make up one square centimeter. It is impossible to predict from what spot the next electron will come, or when it will come: only the average number of electrons released is proportional to the intensity of illumination; some electrons may come immediately after the light uniformly illuminating the target is turned on, even if it is so faint that it would take hours before an emitting spot has received from the light as much energy as the electron carries away. To explain this, *Einstein (1879-1955)* proposed in 1905 to disregard the crucial experiments which had established the wave theory of light and to interpret light as consisting of tiny arrows, 'photons', each carrying one of Planck's quanta. The energy a photon carries is then inversely proportional to the wavelength of the light. Photons would leave their sources at irregular intervals and in random directions, and the photo-electric effect would be produced when a photon hits a suitable atom and transfers its energy to the electron tied to the atom. This explains the photo-electric effect, but now the propagation of light becomes a mystery.

A number of other observations and experiments made it clear that the particle and the wave concepts of light cannot be reconciled. One of these concerns the size of the photons. Good telescopes show progressively more detail the larger the diameter of the main optical element, such as the reflector. This, according to the wave theory of light, is because more of the wave front is accepted by a large reflector. As astronomical telescopes have successfully been constructed with reflectors of 2m diameter, the particle theory of light suggests that the photon incorporating the wave must have at least this diameter whereas the photo-electric effect had shown it to be no larger than the atom.

Of the many discoveries which threw sharp light and shade on to the atomic scene, and which contributed to the breakdown of causality, only two more will be mentioned here: the Compton effect, because of the deep impression it made when it was discovered in 1923, as the most direct evidence for the particle nature of electromagnetic radiation, and electron diffraction, as direct evidence for the wave nature of the electron.

X-rays and X-ray spectroscopy were by 1923 well established. X-rays were known to be part of the electromagnetic wave spectrum which extends from long radio waves to the gamma rays of radioactivity. Compton discovered that the wave length of X-rays is increased when they are scattered by light materials such as paraffin, and that this increase depends on the angle by which the rays are deflected. Electromagnetic *waves* should not suffer such changes; but if the X-rays are taken as *photons*, with energies and momenta as assigned to them by Einstein, then the events in question are interpreted as random collisions of photons with electrons, and an elementary calculation gives the observed values for the change in wavelength.

Soon afterwards faith in the particle nature of the electron received a severe shock when in 1924 Louis de Broglie announced that quantitative data of the hydrogen spectrum could be obtained by treating the electron of the hydrogen atom as a wave phenomenon. It had indeed been known since the times of Fermat and Maupertuis that there was much in common between the motion of particles subject to forces and waves progressing through media of changing refractive index. In 1925 Elsasser suggested that cathode rays should, as waves, give rise to interference phenomena of the kind observed with X-rays. Such phenomena were then actually observed in 1927 by Davisson and Germer and in 1928 by G.P. Thomson. So, by 1927 the views physicists had had of the nature of the objects of their studies and their orderly behaviour had become blurred. Moreover, a new field of physical studies, and perhaps a threat to humanity, had begun to arise from the study of radioactivity. In 1919 the first transmutation of a non-radioactive element was observed when nitrogen was exposed to alpha rays. Blackett then studied these rare processes with the cloud chamber. Ten years later, Bothe and Becker, Irene Curie and Joliot and Chadwick discovered that an uncharged elementary particle of the mass of the hydrogen nucleus (the proton) was emitted by beryllium under alpha particle bombardment. The existence of such particles explained at last why chemically identical atoms could have different weights. Such atoms are known as isotopes. Nuclei were now understood to be composed of these new particles, named neutrons, and protons which carry unit positive charge. The number of protons determines the chemical properties, and that of protons and neutrons together the atomic weight. A nitrogen atom, e.g. is composed of 7 protons and 7 or 8 neutrons, giving it the atomic weight 14 or 15. In addition, neutrons provided the ideal projectile for interfering with atomic nuclei: the alpha particles used by Rutherford and Blackett are rarely successful in transmuting nitrogen nuclei because both the alpha particles and the nuclei carry positive charges and hence repel each other so that they cannot easily come into intimate contact; a neutron approaching a nucleus experiences no repulsive force and can therefore enter it unretarded and un-deflected.

Enrico Fermi (1901-1954) was the first to realise the potential efficiency of neutrons, and within a few months he and his collaborators in Rome transmuted a large number of nuclei. This threw much light on the structure of nuclei but technically it was still an inefficient process. But when in 1938 Hahn, Strassmann, Meitner and Frisch discovered that some heavy elements exposed to neutrons split up with the release of more neutrons, a process came in sight which would maintain itself if care were taken that of the neutrons released at least one could initiate a further process. Thus began the age of the atomic bomb and of nuclear power stations and thus research in nuclear physics and sub-nuclear particles became a matter of military and technological priority. Money poured into such studies on an unprecedented scale. ·

The experiments had shown that the old list of elements was almost complete chemically but that almost every chemical element could be had in a number of radioactive variants, useful tools for chemical and biological research. The physicist's interest then turned to the question whether the old list of elementary particles, electrons, protons, neutrons, photons was complete and if they could be crushed or split by an increased effort. Machinery was devised by which such particles could be turned into tools of mutual destruction, by giving them energies equivalent to those which they could acquire from an electric power source of many thousand million volts. It then turned out that all known particles could by sufficiently violent impact be destroyed, that is trans-formed into electromagnetic radiation, or into other known particles; and that, under other conditions, particles old and new are created from electromagnetic radiation.

It will be realised that such particles, being more elementary than atoms, cannot have many properties. They may or may not have an electric charge (the same or the opposite of that of the electron); they may or may not have a mass (a rest mass); they have a spin and an average lifetime after which they transform themselves into other particles. They are further characterised by what it is they change into. There are a few other essential properties, such as the forces through which they interact with other particles. Perhaps twenty such elementary particles can be distinguished. The transformations are controlled by a few general and some specific rules.

So to the chance in the *movement* of particles, high energy physics has added the chance of their *creation* and *destruction*. On the other hand it must be allowed that the experimenting, for all its power, is crude: it consists at best in giving bunches of particles the desired high energy and then letting them bash against other bunches of particles, hoping that some will collide head-on, so that the experimenting itself introduces an element of randomness.

Let us now go back to 1913 to relate how the natural philosophers reacted to the then new knowledge.

In 1913 *Niels Bohr (1885-1962)* presented his model of the atom. Bohr showed that the spectra of at least the simpler atoms such as hydrogen could be calculated with great precision, on the basis of a peculiar set of assumptions. He took Rutherford's result that atoms have a small positively charged nucleus which is surrounded by electrons. Then he argued that the electrons, being attracted by the nucleus, must circle around the nucleus as do the planets around the sun. The snag is that according to electrical lore the circling electrons should steadily lose energy by radiation and thus, going into smaller and smaller circles, collapse into the nucleus. This Bohr ruled out by assigning to the electron a number of definite orbits, with energies E_1, E_2.., which he calculated by a formula embodying Planck's h. When the electron collapses from one orbit to a smaller one the atom emits the excess of energy $E_2 - E_1 = \triangle E$ as radiation such as is found in the observed spectra. The model was fantastically successful in reproducing and forecasting many experimental details, but there were also persistent failures.

Bohr's atomic model at first received an ambiguous welcome. Einstein greeted it as one of the great discoveries, whereas Laue considered as intolerable the violation of a fundamental rule of Maxwell's electrodynamics.

On the whole the model was accepted with some misgivings, but these were, for a decade, drowned by the flood of successes which its elaboration by Bohr, Sommerfeld and others had in interpreting spectral data.

In this way a climate of opinion was created in which new ways of looking at atomic problems were explored. Bohr himself never left any doubt that he considered his model as provisional and its deficiencies as obvious. In any case, it activated much experimental work related to atomic physics.

In the meantime the search for a more consistent description of the atom went on. In 1924 *L. de Broglie (born 1892)* conceived the idea of applying to electrons the mathematics of waves, and succeeded, for hydrogen, in reproducting Bohr's energy levels.

When we talk of particles, we think in the first instance of individual objects, such as tennis balls, apples, boxes etc., reduced to a size below visibility. With visibility the particle loses smell, colour, etc. It retains geometrical properties, it still occupies a finite space; there is some kind of bang when it collides with another particle, and it may leave a track when passing through a medium; we see tracks of high-flying aeroplanes, even if we do not see the plane. This is the kind of evidence we have for the particle character of the electron.

·Now we also encounter objects which are not individual, such as the sea: fishes and divers can move through it; air was recognised as in this respect similar, offering less resistance to the passage of individual objects than water. We observe spreading ripples on the surface of a pond when we throw a stone into it; these waves carry the message of the incident without a material messenger; for the water does not flow with the message. The next step is to realise that similar waves can also exist in the *interior* of continuous media; sound was early recognised to be of this kind. That the phenomenon of light should be interpreted as waves was discussed above. Here, the evidence lacks one of the supports which is available for sound. Sound can be produced by vibrating a disc, or a reed, while no equivalent means of producing light is available. The remarkable thing is that most of the properties of light can be explained, devices can be designed, and new phenomena forecast from the wave character alone without specifying the medium. (It did of course help when this medium was identified with that of electric and magnetic forces.)

De Broglie could therefore discuss matter waves without specifying the medium of which the waves were waves, the medium just being the medium of matter-waves. Nor is it at all clear how this medium could be further elucidated, without introducing something requiring no less elucidation.

The development of de Broglie's idea is due, in the first instance, to *Schrödinger (1887-1961)* who founded *wave mechanics* in a series of papers published in 1926. What had been a particular case became, through Schrödinger, a general theory which threw its light on many aspects of atomic theory. Schrödinger's differential equations are constructed in the light of the forces which had been believed to act on the electron particle.

Schrödinger thought at first that wave-mechanics would explain all atomic phenomena, including quantum effects and electron interferences, on a uniform causal-pictorial basis. It was, however, soon seen that the electron interference effect was exceptional in its close resemblance to optical interference phenomena. The wave function to which was allotted the Greek letter ψ is in general complex, i.e. it contains a number multiplied by $\sqrt{-1}$, a symbol which has mathematical but no direct physical significance. When, however, by a simple mathematical operation an expression written as $\psi\psi^*$ which is free from this deficiency is derived from ψ the close optical analogy is lost. *M. Born (1882-1970)* then came to the conclusion that this expression describes the *probability* of finding the point electrons. It follows that laws no longer directly determine the motion of particles. 'The motion of particles conforms to the laws of probability but the probability itself is propagated in accordance with the laws of causality'. (Born, 1926). This interpretation was modelled after Einstein's idea of the relation between light waves and photons. It marks the beginning of the recognition of chance as a concept in modern science.

Before that, in 1925, *Heisenberg (1901-1976)* had proposed to abandon all models by the principle that 'No entity should be introduced in physics unless it is possible to devise an experiment, at least of an ideal nature, which will demonstrate the existence of that entity. No quantity should be introduced unless some means even if only of an ideal nature, can be devised to measure it'. The idea was to create a mathematical apparatus through which observed quantities such as a frequency and intensity of spectral lines could be calculated without recourse to recondite features such as Bohr orbits. Such apparatus did in fact exist in the mathematics of matrices. It was later found that Heisenberg's method was equivalent to Schödinger's wave mechanics.

Developing his idea, Heisenberg enunciated in 1927 the 'principle of indeterminacy' or 'uncertainty principle' which teaches that neither the location nor the momentum (the product of mass and velocity) of a particle can be determined with unlimited precision. According to the principle, the product of the uncertainty of a co-ordinate and of the conjugate momentum is never smaller than Planck's constant h. As h is very small, this relation does not affect any measurement which a physicist or an engineer can actually carry out. Even the smallest object visible under a high-power microscope can be explored to any accuracy the microscope can provide. But Heisenberg is concerned with sub-microscopic, or 'elementary', particles. Then the principle fairly describes a situation such as that facing an observer who wishes to describe the position and the speed of the crest of a wave - in particular of a wave as given by Schrödinger's equation. The uncertainty principle, whilst not solving the paradoxes mentioned above, indicates the extent to which particle- and wave-models can separately be trusted, or the extent to which measurement can, under quantum conditions, be successful: measurement itself destroys some of the knowledge learned from earlier experiments. In classical physics, a precise simultaneous determination of location and momentum is possible because the tools of the observer can be small compared with the size and the mass of the object and therefore incapable of influencing it. But atomic dimensions are the smallest to be had, so that no tools can be found delicate enough to leave the object unchanged. Many examples - such as the problem of locating an electron by means of a hypothetical microscope - have been discussed which illustrate the validity of Heisenberg's principle. The discussion of the cases involved is curiously different from the discussion normally carried out in physics research; it makes one think of the deliberations by which a criminal gang would plan a bank robbery, or a detective agency would try to unravel it.

While it is generally recognised that Heisenberg's principle represents a new fundamental insight, its interpretation is not obvious. First, it can be argued that the principle is as much a restriction on chance as it is on causality, allowing only some play in the specification of a particle's location and momentum. Then, should we conclude that this play is a property of the particles themselves, or that the particles have precise co-ordinates which, however, are in principle unobservable in their precision? Does the principle, speaking of location and momentum, imply the definite adoption of the particle model? Are we encouraged to allow the particle to change its momentum without cause? Heisenberg himself suggested that the principle does not apply to the past, because the momentum of a particle can be calculated from its location at two successive times. Reichenbach (1944) thought that description of the unobserved path of a particle is a more remote inference than the parameters 'directly' measured and can therefore be saddled with less trustworthy attributes. He held that the principle states a limitation of the measure-ability of simultaneous values existing at the time when we have knowledge of them.

Atomism first reduced the variety of observed events to a small number of inferred ones so that necessity could replace causality. Quantum theory provides another angle on atomism: it shows that atomic events are too delicate to be accounted for rigorously, so that chance robs necessity of its complete control. The paradox of Heisenberg's principle rests on his applying positivistic notions to atoms, which after all belong to the most deviously inferred entities. But even more paradoxical was Bohr's response to the new development. He introduced the notion of *complementarity*, a notion which Jammer (1966) has called a new logical instrument.

Bohr starts by pointing out that the Schrödinger-Heisenberg development contributed to the scope rather than the understanding of atomistics. Even the uncertainty principle only formalises previous ideas. The essential point is that whereas in classical physics causality and space-time description are united, in quantum theory they are complementary and mutually exclusive. Consider, for example, the orbits which according to the earlier atomic model are traced out by the electrons surrounding the atomic nucleus. The orbits describe stationary states in space and time. They could be observed only by directing some radiation at them, but this radiation, if it leads to an observation, must throw the electron out of its orbit. It follows that the orbits are in principle not observable and that the concept of cause and effect cannot meaningfully be applied to them. If now the radiation causes the electrons to 'jump' from one orbit to another one, this transition is a discontinuous change which it has not been possible to describe in terms of a movement is space and time. Hence have grown the opposing notions of waves and particles. The uncertainty relation tells us the price we have to pay for applying to the description of a physical phenomenon two categories of notions which strictly speaking are contradictory. The very nature of the quantum theory thus forces us to regard co-ordination in space-time and the claims of causality, the union of which characterises the classical theory, as complementary but exclusive features of the description, symbolising the idealisation of observation and definition respectively.

The quantum condition entails that any elementary measurement changes the object, the more so the higher the attempted precision. The situation, Bohr suggests, is analogous to the difficulties of psychological introspection on which the philosophers have commented. The self changes as we explore it because the explored self is different from the unexplored self and, in the last analysis, because in this psychological situation the separation of subject and object is lost. In quantum physics the separation of subject and object is lost because the means of exploration and the explored elementary particle have comparable masses.

It is here relevant to quote a reference made by Bohr in 1949 to a discussion at the Solvay Congress in 1928.

'The question was whether as to the occurrence of individual effects we·should adopt a terminology proposed by Dirac, that we were concerned with the choice on the part of nature, or, as suggested by Heisenberg, we should say that we have to do with a choice on the part of the observer, constructing the measuring instruments, and reading their recording. Any such terminology would, however, appear dubious, since on the one hand it is hardly reasonable to endow nature with volition in the ordinary sense while on the other hand, it is certainly not possible for the observer to influence the events which may appear under the conditions he has arranged. To my mind, there is no other alternative than to admit that, in this field of experience, we are dealing with individual phenomena and that our possibilities of handling the measuring instrument allow us only to make a choice between different complementary types of phenomena we·want to study.'

These ideas became the creed of a large fraction of the quantummechanical community. There was also a fringe to this community, led by Louis de Broglie and not discouraged by Einstein, who kept on searching for 'hidden parameters' through which strict causality could be re-introduced.

In a set of interviews with prominent physicists published in book form in 1934, but probably referring to considerably earlier dates, J.W.N. Sullivan had found that Planck and Painlevé then still considered that indeterminacy was only a temporary device, but Prince Louis de Broglie gave an answer almost identical with that of Eddington. Both suggested that the scientific outlook which assumed that nature formed a perfectly deterministic scheme must be given up. Eddington in his 1927 lectures on *The*

Nature of the Physical World had stated that physics is no longer pledged to a scheme of deterministic laws and had solemnly concluded: 'Science thereby withdraws its moral opposition to free will'. Planck, on the other hand, had written in 1923 that 'no physicist should have any doubts that the quantum hypothesis would eventually find its exact expression in equations which could then be taken as a precise formulation of the causal laws'. Planck believed that the 'assumption of causality without exception, of a perfect determinism, is the condition of scientific knowledge.' He still persisted in this in 1926. In 1929, however, he considered, albeit with sorrow, the possibility of a breakdown of causality. Only in 1932 did he accept that causality could no longer be maintained in its classical formulation.

Einstein, however, supported by the famous Dutch physicist *H.A. Lorentz (1853-1928)*, was not prepared to believe in chance. He voiced his objections against what could now be labelled the conservative interpretation of quantum theory, as soon as Heisenberg put forward his idea. 'Marvellous', I heard him say after Heisenberg's 1927 lecture, 'what ideas the young people have these days. - Was sich die jungen Leute alles ausdenken - But I do not believe a word of it'. Einstein held to a strictly deterministic view from his earliest days onwards and essentially maintained it to his last days in Princeton.

In his famous 1917 article on radioactive equilibrium we find the remark 'the weakness of the theory lies in the fact that, on the one hand, no closer connection with the wave concept is obtainable and that, on the other hand, it leaves to chance the time and the direction of the elementary processes'. Then, Bohr reports from the 1928 Solvay Congress a discussion which Ehrenfest and he had with Einstein: 'on his side Einstein mockingly asked us whether we could really believe that the Providential Authorities resorted to dice playing (ob der liebe Gott würfelt)'. And in a letter to Born he wrote in 1944 'In our scientific expectation we have become antipodes - you believe in God playing dice and I in perfect laws in a world of things existing as real objects, which I try to grasp in a wildly speculative way'.

This conviction led Einstein to conclude that Bohr's notion of physical reality and his idea of the complementarity of spatial and causal description were unsound, that the quantum theory gives an incomplete representation of the physical world and should eventually be superseded by a different theory. Einstein exemplified his point by insisting on the significance of the fact that the instant of decay of a radioactive atom can be recorded with great precision, whereas the theory does not allow giving a date at all. He did not deny, however, that the statistical interpretation of the quantum theory was self-consistent, as he worte in a letter to Born in 1953:

> 'It is only necessary to assume that the ψ - function refers to an ensemble and not to an individual case. True, on this view, the description of a single system is incomplete, but this becomes acceptable provided the complete description of a single system is not completely covered by deterministic laws (for the temporal sequence). Then there is no need to follow Bohr's interpretation that a reality independent of the probable observer does not exist. I do not believe that this quite consistent view will be final, but I propose that it is the only one which does justice to the mechanism of the probabilistic quantum theory.'

Einstein obviously hoped that the quantum theory as developed over the last 50 years could be replaced; his objection to it was not based on physical reasoning but was rooted in his faith in strict causality.

7

Taking up the Dialogue

Brunschvicg referred to the history of causality as to a continued dialogue between man and nature. Let us now take up the dialogue ourselves - often turning back to the earlier partners by way of a dialogue between man and man.

Causes are exceptions

The notions of cause and effect, as well as those of chance and necessity, are inevitable. Whatever discalimers of causes may have been made in the past, all active life is based on causality. Vital concepts such as faith and planning, revenge and repentance would lose sense without causality. The physician diagnoses the cause of the symptoms, the coroner finds the cause of the death. He may err, but a sudden death will have had a cause. Causal relations are the burden of detective novels and are studied in historical investigations. Gilbert attributed the rotation of the earth to terrestrial magnetism. Galileo deplored his own ignorance of the virtue causing a stone to drop. It is the joy of the experimental physicist and the bane of the student to find unexpected results: their causes must be found by either. So did Röntgen discover X-rays when, experimenting with discharge tubes, he observed the luminescence of some distant screens.

Although these examples refer to complex events, *one* cause is quoted for each event and, normally, one only. The illumination of a situation through the cause rests on its one-ness. The question is essentially and rightly to find *the* cause, not a system of the world. At an inquest the coroner is not asked for a physiological analysis; malaria is caused by a specific germ carried by a specific mosquito; the leak in the vacuum system is at a particular joint etc. The selectiveness does not mean that a cause is a subjective affair because you can choose your word.

Now, if the cause is one element of a rich past, how is it selected? It does not help very much to allow for this selectivity by distinguishing between essential and irrelevant factors, as L. Tisza (1963) suggests. Rather, the reference frequently made to repetition as confirming a cause could be inverted. An event, or a property, which differs from comparable events or properties has its cause in some prior event or connected property which is also exceptional. It is not, or not essentially, the repetition which confirms the cause, but the dissenting element in the repetition. For example, people normally do not die walking in the High Street; the man who did, was hit by a falling chimney pot. Or, a technician operating a vacuum plant has the experience that it takes one hour's pumping for the pressure to drop to the operating value. When it fails to do so the failure is perhaps caused by a leak in a connection. The experimenter will test this by a simple manipulation - tightening the connector: if the vacuum then imporves the cause of the failure has been found. Whilst the role of exception has not explicitly been assigned to causes, Aristotle's examples confirm this contention. Most of the time, for example, the moon is not eclipsed, a pilot is usually available to bring the ship to harbour. In the exceptional case of the eclipse we find the cause related to a particular position of the moon; the pilot causes the ship's wreck by his exceptional absence. Again, for Newton the normal condition of a body is that of constant velocity. If it deviates - the exception - Newton finds the cause in a force.

It is no contradiction to see the cause in the *exception* (a heritage from primitive man) and to confirm the assignment of a cause by finding repetition of the sequence if circumstances prevent confirmation by manipulation. If walking in the High Street were a rare event we might connect the High Street directly with the walker's sudden death; but walking in the High Street is an often repeated exercise, which normally has no deleterious effect on the walker; and chimney pots fall but rarely. The sequence may be one of a family of such sequences, and, as the cause always refers to a particular aspect, the sequences need not be *exactly* alike. Medical diagnosis is often based on the similarity of case histories, and in nature studies a repetition of sequences is normally sought.

Contiguity and Laws of Nature

The repetition of exceptions alone does not prove the cause. The assignment of a cause to an effect must be verified by the discovery of *intermediate links,* disclosing a contiguity of stages. Contiguity was discussed by Aristotle, Hume and many others following them. Discontinuity breaks the causal chain: this is why the first light of the quantum concept was greeted with so much

72

suspicion. Contiguity as proof of a causal relation comes prominently into play in medical diagnosis and in historical studies.

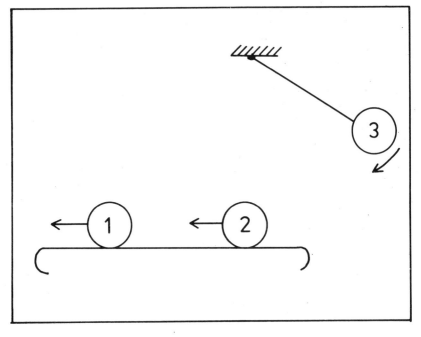

Fig. 1

Now it is important to see that this contiguity can be established by observation or alternatively by reference to *'laws of nature'*. Look at the following simple example illustrated in Figure 1. We have two balls at rest, and a third ball suspended as a pendulum in the same vertical plane, locked but threatening the second ball. Suddenly, the ball (1) begins to move, the release of the pendulum (ball 3) being the cause. Elementary dynamics, the laws of inertia and of collisions teach us how and with what speed the pendulum drops, pushes ball (2) which then moves steadily until it collides with ball (1) and sets it in motion. The contiguity of the cause (the release of the pendulum) and the effect (ball (1) beginning to move) is provided by the laws of collisions and inertia. Indeed, it can be argued that it is precisely the function of laws of nature to describe what happens 'by itself', i.e. without outside, in particular human, intervention or in the absence of 'exceptional' events. It is not, however, necessary that a law should refer to a change with time, or even that the knowledge of nature be condensed into a 'law' in order to serve this purpose. We may attribute the high electronic conductivity of a specimen of germanium to the addition of arsenic to the melt as the cause - if this is what was done - because we know that arsenic atoms readily release an electron, without formulating this knowledge into a law. Laws of nature are therefore complementary to causes and not only, as Comte had suggested, alternatives, in the sense that the notion of causes has been superseded by that of laws. This can also be seen from the often emphasised asymmetry of the cause-effect relation which has no counterpart in laws of nature. A leak in a vacuum system can cause the pressure to stabilise at 10^{-6} torr, but a stable pressure cannot cause a leak. An electric current deflects a magnetic needle, but a needle deflected does not cause a current to flow. Comte was of course right in so far as laws operate in the absence of causes. This was in fact noted by Aristotle when he discussed what nature does by itself. In the absence of exceptional circumstances we agree with primitive man not to search for causes but we still see the laws of nature satisfied.

Aristotle had already surmised that the quest for causes is not always justified and that natural developments or regular changes cannot be analysed in terms of cause-effect relations. The child is not the cause of the adult, and the sunset not the cause of the sunrise. Any sequence of events fully interpreted by 'laws of nature' is outside a cause-effect analysis and the progress of the sciences tends to enlarge the range of cause-less sequences. Of this, the geodesic lines of the general theory of relativity provide a striking example. The path of any moving particle in a gravitational field is the 'straightest' line allowing for the disturbing effects of other bodies. For the Newtonian physicist the path was subject to two different conditions, it was an uncaused straight line affected by causes, mainly the gravitational forces due to other bodies.

On the other hand, given a cause, the quest for the effect can fail on account of the phenomenon which, above, it was proposed to call forked causality. While this appears to play a decisive role in atomic physics where causality should become necessity, indications of forked causality are frequently seen in everyday experience. The same act, the discharging of a gun, can have a wide spectrum of results between just being a bang and leading to a major war.

The faith in the existence of a cause does not however imply a faith in strict causality. This would require utterly simplified conditions. If we had a demon playing with two elementary particles, who at a given instant throws particle I at particle II and then retires, we would expect strict causality to prevail: the aimed throw being the complete cause of the subsequent collision. We can at our peril relax this condition and let a scientific experimenter, a physicist in particular, play in his laboratory the role of such a demon, building up his apparatus protected from external influences, with the minimum of uncontrolled parameters. The art of experimenting has been specially invented to make causality work. As soon as we leave this ivory tower, we must in fact restrict ourselves to a particular cause, i.e. the exception, and give up the idea of making the cause complete. When in Thornton Wilder's novel the bridge of San Luis Rey collapsed and the people on it perished, the cause of the collapse and the recent history of the victims could be established. But many questions were left unanswered. What had condemned them to sudden death? Why were they on the bridge at the critical minute? What emotion had made one traveller hurry to get on to the bridge, what had prevented another one from being on it at the instant of collapse? There are too many contributing factors on too many levels to make causality strict or complete.

So it boils down to this: when we have an effect that is an event which singles itself out like a picture in a frame, we shall find a cause. If affairs just run on, we can normally point to some laws of nature. Only Hume's rule: same cause same effect, must be open to doubt.

Can such a causality now be 'established' in Hume's sense? How could it be established? Hume himself was not satisfied with the psychological answer, which he gave himself; quite rightly not, because psychology is concerned with facts, not with epistemological proofs. Maine de Biran also does not meet this objection. Kant's reasoning and Dewey's discussion are on a different level, but neither Kant nor Dewey would have satisfied Hume: as causality is not a logical necessity, to establish it can mean only reduction to a proposition or a set of propositions which in turn would be subject to further quests. Of this type are the suggestions to relate causality to laws of conservation such as *ex nihilo nihil fit.*

Causality and Time

In much of physics, as for instance in optics, thermodynamics and statics, no reference at all is made to time. Parmenides and Plato considered a reference to time almost obscene. No law of physics contains time explicitly - Maxwell pronounced that neither time nor location *can* explicitly enter any physical law. But the most readily quoted laws describe *rates of change with time*; they contain either second or first differential coefficients with respect to time. The laws of dymanics belong to the first group while the second group includes the laws controlling the flow of heat and fluids and the laws of thermodynamics, laws which, it was thought, could be derived rigorously from those of the first group. Planck called them *'statistical'* to distinguish them from the *'causal'* laws of the first group. Statistical laws give values of averages, but individual results are not expected to satisfy the laws exactly, although normally the deviations are below the observational errors. 'Causal' laws always have two solutions differing by the sign of the time co-ordinate. The planetary movements would equally satisfy the laws of dynamics if all planets were to reverse the direction of their motion, so that sets of positions taken at different times could be ordered into two sequences which differ by the direction of time only. Eddington concluded that the 'arrow of time' is defined only by the second law of thermodynamics - the most prominent member of the second group of laws. The relevant point is that both types of laws connect states at different times and that applying the laws of classical dynamcis alone it is impossible to tell the past from the future.

Kant had argued that the cause-effect relation establishes the direction of time. According to Born, time may or may not enter causality. Margenau and Bunge are definite about the fact that the cause precedes the effect. Let us examine some examples.

Neglecting the finite velocity of light, of which Aristotle was ignorant, the eclipse and the shadow of the earth causing it are simultaneous. But a gale which causes the destruction of a bridge definitely precedes it; and excess pressure precedes the explosion, and the firing of the gun precedes the death of the victim. We are not irritated by the apparent absence of a time interval in the first example, but we are able to account for the interval in the second group of examples by reference to laws of nature; causes are singularities in the chain of events, perhaps human acts or 'acts of God', whereas the chains themselves are sequences which proceed by themselves and are controlled by the laws of physics.

According to the theory of relativity, the time difference between events depends on their distance apart and the state of motion of the observer with respect to the events. An event may precede a second event for one observer, and be subsequent to it for another one. This does not, however, lead to a reversal of the cause-effect sequence. For, if an event A, at $x = x_1$ has caused an event B at $x = x_2$, this action cannot have been propagated from x_1 to x_2 in less time than it takes a ray of light to travel this distance. The theory of relativity then shows that for no observer will B precede A.

Let us conclude that the effect cannot precede the cause. Then, if even a single cause-effect relation is found with a time interval between cause and effect, the effect must be later than the cause and the direction of the time is fixed for ever and we can check if our clocks go forwards or backwards. If this is what Kant meant, his assertion that causality establishes temporal order could be convincing. But Eddington's criticism applies if causality is related to the exclusive rule of classical dynamics.

Necessity and Prediction

Democritus' inspiration that a completely determined and lawful world must be a world of atoms in empty space has not always been appreciated. The reader will readily remember many prominent voices postulating a world completely determined by a large variety of causes - a trap into which even a thinker as penetrating as Borel (1914) seems to have fallen. But it is impossible to visualise, outside a monistic-atomistic system, how the whole universe could at any instant be taken as the cause of all separate events - how 'not a single hair of a bumble bee can be changed without changing the whole world' ('Il n'est pas en effet possible de modifier un seul phénomène sans modifier tous les autres.')

When Leucippus or Democritus conceived the idea of atoms and necessity, they had no information on which to base an estimate of the size of atoms, their variety, or the forces between them. They could have had no notion of the magnitude of the effort needed to transform their ideas into detailed knowledge, and they might even have despised it as no business for gentlemen. But the attempt to understand nature on Democritus' terms has been a highly successful venture.

Nor could the ancient atomists have had a clear idea of how necessity determines sequences of events. Should necessity be equated with the Fates, divine norms and regularities of nature? After the discovery of mathematical physics we think of necessity as the complete control of events by a complete set of laws of nature, such as the laws of conservation of energy and momentum, Maxwell's equations, etc. We are quite satisfied that we have a clear idea of sequences occurring by necessity, i.e. according to laws, in spite of voices, quoted below (in the appendix), which deny the validity of a distinction between necessity and happening. Curiously enough, no codex exists of such laws, and in general the scientist's attitude to laws - as distinct from lawfulness - is somewhat detached. Not long ago a well-known physicist published a popular book on the laws of nature, describing the various laws. Perhaps a year or two later he chaired a discussion on the Third Programme about the discovery of a phenomenon violating 'one of the most cherished laws of nature' - which he had happened to forget even to mention in his book.

Just as necessity tends to invade actuality in experiments, so there is no logical reason to exclude causality from the atomic scene. If we can fix an event as cause, such as a collision, and a second event as effect, such as the emission of radiation, a cause-effect relation will exist. The thought that this world of many colours, thoughts and emotions, could be reduced to - or *in reality is* - an assembly of a small variety of elementary particles subject to a few rules, has impressed people according to their temperaments as atrocious, intoxicating or paralysing. The important thing is that in such an assembly the sequence of situations and the kinds of influences are rigorously fixed and the variety of changes which can occur is strictly limited. Hence the gap between the atomic order and the world we live in is large, but there are bridges over which necessity flows into the world. First, through laws common to the realm of necessity and the world of causes, such as those of inertia, attraction between bodies and of conservation. Secondly, large sections of the doctrines which used to be taught as properties of matter and which now go by the name of material science, including for example the kinetic theory of gases, and, of course, nuclear power, are witnesses of a success-ful penetration of atomic physics into the world of engineering.

Now, the scenario of atomic necessity includes continuous quantities which for their definition require an infinity of data. This, as Philipp Frank and others have claimed, contradicts the idea of necessity. Moreover, it has been suggested (Borel, 1914) that the calculation of the movement of even a few gas molecules would require a range of initial information which surpasses all imagination. For, he argues, consider a gas filled container and in particular one molecule set on a collision course with another one. A small change in the angle of approach is, on collision, multiplied by a large factor, say tenfold. As a result, after one second, that is after 10^9 collisions, the initial deviation is multiplied 10^{10^9} times.

So, *prediction* in any elementary, i.e. complete, sense is impossible. But this conclusion, as the fear of continuous quantities, is arrived at by a rigorous pursuit of a strictly deterministic physics, so that it cannot possibly be used as an argument against determinism. It only confirms that predictability and determinism are different notions, the first belonging to the consciousness of the observer and the second one to the way the world functions. At most it could be said that prediction must be based on orderliness in nature, in addition to the presence of an intelligent being, whereas nature could well be orderly without such a being. Also, natural processes are not elucidated by reference to prediction, whereas predictability can be explained in terms of natural properties. Margenau has reinforced this consider-ation by elaborating a model of a world not ruled by laws but governed by an irrational demon who decides every Sunday what is going to happen during the following week. A favoured priest to whom he communicates his decision is obviously in a position to make valid predictions. The Roman *haruspices* may be quoted as forerunners of Margenau's priest.

But, of course, it is not really this kind of prediction which is here in question. The reference to prediction sharply illuminates the difference between causality and necessity. Causality covers man's need for prediction, action, thought, science and business. The course of necessity which resists prediction may well be left unpredicted.

Hiding places of chance

However sound the concept of necessity may be logically, it is powerless against the double onslaught of Epicurus' objections (which have never been disproved) and the experimental evidence of randomness in nature. Chance is incomprehensible, it cannot be understood, it contradicts the spirit of science just as gambling contradicts the economic sense of a bourgeois society. Hence it must be tucked away, out of daily reach, say in Monaco or Baden Baden. In science too, chance must be encapsulated, prominently hidden away. Awful types of hazard have been talked of - frightening miracles, the spontaneous generation of small animals. But just as in Monaco the hazard is limited to the loss of your stake or the gain of a small multiple of it, so in the new science chance is restricted to the occurrence of particular angles, places or times. How can such chance be incorporated in a systematic description of nature?

It was Born's idea that the amplitude of the wave function $\psi\,(x,y,z)$ gives the probability of finding the electron in the neighbourhood of x,y,z. This interpretation implies that the electron is, as a particle, at any instant at a particular place, so that the uncertainty of where to find it can refer only to the ignorance of the observer. Now suppose that the observer actually *finds* the particle in one particular place. When the particle has been found, the probability of its being where found changes to 1, and that of its being elsewhere to 0. Simply through being tested, the wave function appears to 'collapse' or to 'contract', as this phenomenon has been called. Note also that this change does not depend on any effect the tools of observation may have on the electron. (As pointed out by Einstein, Podolski and Rosen (1935) and recently exemplified by Renninger (1960), particles can sometimes be located without their momentum being changed.) Must we conclude that the wave function exists only in the mind of the observer? Acquiring knowledge can, of course, in many ways affect expectation. The mathematics of probability began when the Chevalier de Méré asked Pascal (1623-1662) (Problème des parties) how to divide the pool after an unfinished game. The partners A and B alternately toss a coin, and the pool is taken by the partner who first collects ten heads. At the beginning the partners have equal chances. Let after a while A have 8 and B have 5 heads. How much greater is A's chance of winning the pool than B's? A bookmaker taking bets on the outcome of the game must offer equal odds so long as he has no knowledge of the progress of the game, but should alter his offer when he learns of A's 8 and B's 5 heads. The probability of B's winning has changed, but only for the observer who is kept informed. Is probability here an objective datum at the beginning of the game, and does it become subjective as the game proceeds?

The similarity between the bookmaker and Born's observer is, however, restricted. The bookmaker's situation is realistic. Born's observer is in a totally unrealistic situation. For an electron spinning around the nucleus cannot be located.

W. Gibbs (1902) faced a situation similar to that of Born's observer when he studied the statistics of thermodynamic systems. He conceived the idea of an *ensemble*, and idea through which the probabilities occurring in statistical mechanics lose any subjective connotation. Think, for example, of a gas in a container, at given temperature and pressure. For the ordinary observer, this defines all properties he could be interested in. But the positions of the individual molecules and their velocities always change, the number of possible values and combinations is exceedingly large, and they will, in the last resort, determine the properties observed. Now think of a very large number of such gas-filled containers, each one representing a particular, one may say frozen, set of locations and velocities. Gibbs called this multitude of replicas an *ensemble*. A set is represented in the ensemble normally more than once, the number of times it is represented being proportional to the probability of finding it in the original assembly of molecules. The observed properties of the gas can then be calculated as averages over the ensemble. Physically, the ensemble could be thought of as the same object, snap-shot infinitely often, at different times, or repeated infinitely many times in space. Probability now refers to pointing at random at a member of the ensemble. A second pointing finds the ensemble unchanged, so that we as subjects can no longer affect the probability: the probability belongs to the ensemble, not to the individual member; and hence is not affected by the observation.

In thermodynamics, the members of an ensemble are normally assemblies of many molecules. This is however not essential. We can consider an ensemble of a single atom in different states, or a single electron in an enclosure. The idea of the ensemble has therefore been applied to wave mechanics where the members can be different points in space, represented according to the value of

$\psi\psi^*$. Born's demon is then confronted by the ensemble, and not first with an undisturbed, uncharted sea and then with one in which the island has just been found. The ensemble interpretation frees Born's interpretation of the wave function from the taint of subjectivity. With this interpretation the question of how the wave function manages to control the probability of finding the electron is left open. It has been said that the wave function provides a guiding field, which does not tell us much. It can also be argued that the experiment envisaged, the location of the electron in its Bohr orbit by means of a special microscope, is totally unrealistic. Not only would it need a demon to arrange the experiment, but even a demon might give up after considering that, as Margenau has pointed out, an electron, taken as a real point particle, would spin around the nucleus at about 10^{16} times a second which is too fast to be located by any means.

So it comes to this: physics is not demonology. No physicist has ever carried out an experiment in which his subjectivity has (logically) come into play. We are forced to conclude that the chance and the probability which the wave function indicates are *objective* features in atomic physics. This, of course, though sometimes contested, is not a new idea. Here is a recent statement by de Broglie (1953), the originator of wave mechanics.

'According to a proof given by von Neumann (the author of the leading (1932) textbook on wave mechanics) the probability in wave mechanics cannot be interpreted by hidden variables. Examining this proof anew, I found that it is based on the following postulate: All such probability distributions have physical existence already before an experiment is made by which a particle distribution becomes evident'.

Leaving aside the demon and all his works, let us now enquire how the duality of particles and waves interprets chance, how this duality or complementarity has become the logical form of chance in physics, by looking at phenomena such as atomic collisions, radioactivity and interference phenomena.

Atoms and electrons are, like bricks, rarely alone, but unlike bricks, they are normally in motion so that collisions amongst them are common and their study has become an important field of experimentation. It was to such studies that Born (1926, 1927) originally applied the interpretation of $\psi\psi^*$ as the probability of finding a particle. Experimentally, a beam of one kind of particles is established, and a group of atoms is placed into its path; the number and the velocities of the particles emerging from the group are observed. But the wave-mechanical theory suggests a continuous flow. Hence, in order to interpret the data found, the hail of particles is taken as a continuous stream, carrying the same momentum and energy; the particles lose their identity on becoming waves. The wave interacts with the atoms, i.e. it is perturbed by their field of force, it is scattered. The scattered wave is calculated by the algorithm of wave mechanics, and this is then re-interpreted as a random hail of particles. When they re-emerge from the wave, the deterministic tie with the original particles is lost.

As another example, let us consider the emission of an alpha particle by a radioactive atom. The solution of this problem was first given by Gamow (1928). It is based on a particular property by which waves, both light and matter waves, differ from particles. Remember the fairy tale of the town council which designed a new town hall without windows and then discovered that the hall was dark; so they instructed the townsfolk to assemble on a bright day and to carry the light inside, in buckets and baskets. The tale reports that the attempt failed. Why did it fail? The light carried in did not escape through the walls, but it had to move to and fro between the walls, as light cannot stand still. Each time, however, that it was scattered by the walls, a large fraction disappeared, being absorbed by the surface of the walls. With large particles, say balls or apples, this would not have happened. Particles are not absorbed, they are either reflected or, if the wall is sufficiently low, they can escape over a wall. But a wall for waves can be such that a fraction is repelled, a fraction transmitted and the rest disappears by absorption. Any shop window shows this effect. Such walls are used a great deal in optical experiments, they are known as partly transparent mirrors. In theory, there need not be any absorption in optical reflectors, and corresponding structures for matter waves are in general non-absorbent.

Now consider an alpha particle, as a constituent, encapsulated within the walls of an atomic nucleus. Taken as a particle, its escape cannot be envisaged. Taken as a wave-phenomenon within non-absorbent walls, we can envisage any rate of leakage according to the transparency of the wall. Let a particular kind of radio-active nucleus retain an alpha particle by a wall of such a low transparency that the amount of 'radiation' inside is reduced to half in one year. This is given the observational interpretation that of a very large number of atoms, half 'decay' in one year by the emission of an alpha particle. Any particular atom either stays whole, or it decays suddenly without notice, and the process of emission itself is instantaneous. Again, chance hides itself in the double translation: particle-continuum-particle. The examples of atomic collision and of radioactive emission of alpha particles illustrate how chance is built into quantum mechanics. The early approach was followed by a development to which the name quantum electrodynamics or quantum field theory was given. It is not easy to get or to give a simple idea of it.

Apart from some very subtle discrepancies which were found between the results of wave mechanical calculations and experiments, the early wave mechanical approach could not deal with photons or the high energy particles which had been found in cosmic rays and produced in big accelerators. Photons and the new particles are observed as they are created and destroyed.

The solution of the problem of creation and destruction requires an algorithm which can tackle the carrier of photons, the electromagnetic field, Schrödinger's wave field and the fields which may guide the new particles, in a uniform manner. Hence the name quantum field theory. Its development is largely based on P.A.M. Dirac's early work of putting quantum theory on a relativistic basis. The electromagnetic field is ruled by Maxwell's equations, electrons are subject to quantum conditions by Schrödinger's equation, etc. The common form of describing the properties of fields is based on 18th century dynamics and a formula by which this is translated into the quantum language. The co-operation of different kinds of particles can then be studied by establishing expressions for the combined fields. The passage of energy from one type of field to the other is mathematically expressed by 'operators' which, in the language of particles, denote the probabilities of their destruction and creation. So that chance is now incorporated not only into the movements of the particles but also into their creation and destruction. Note that this chance has an influence on all processes of this kind, and does not act through separate events such as Epicurus' clinamen.

In the light of the development of quantum field theory, let us now 'examine a phenomenon which is impossible, absolutely impossible, to explain in any classical way, and which has in it the heart of quantum mechancis. In reality, it contains the only mystery...' (Feynman 1965). Feynman refers to the following arrangement: a small source of monochromatic light is placed behind a screen with a narrow slit. (Fig. 2a) On passing through the slit the light is deflected so that all regions of a plate placed in front of it have a chance of being hit by a photon. If another slit is opened near the first one, the illumination ceases to be uniform and changes into a pattern of alternating bright and dark fringes: if there are two slits, the photon will avoid certain regions, while still of course, as a particle, it must go through one of the slits, and one only, in order to reach the plate. How then, does it acquire knowledge of the second aperture? The absurdity of this description is obvious. The wave theory of light, on the other hand, whilst explaining the fringe pattern, (Fig. 2b) does not explain the blackening of even a single grain of silver bromide on the plate as was discussed above.

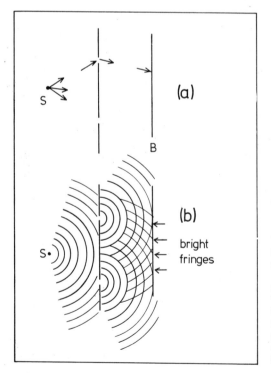

Fig. 2
The 'mystery' of interference

(a) The photon model:
The photon can use only one aperture but it can excite an atom on the screen B.

(b) The wave model:
The wave can pass through two apertures at the same time but it cannot excite atoms. The pattern is explained, but not how it can be observed.

This two-slit experiment is perhaps a paragon of all interference experiments, but in principle it describes only a typical situation. The explanation of a diffraction grating or of any interferometer involves the same difficulty.

It had been suggested (Reichenbach 1944) that the emission and absorption of photons whould be granted the status of phenomena, whereas the path of the photon is arrived at only by an extended inferential chain and represents an (interpolated) 'interphenomenon'. Reichenbach suggests that such interphenomena can always be described in a variety of ways and never without incurring 'causal anomalies' which are typical for and exclusive to quantum physics. Considering the difficulty from a logical rather than from a material point of view, he suggests that one should allow for 'interphenomena' by a three-valued logic in which the classes 'true' and 'false' are supplemented by a class 'indeterminate'. But if we recognise that nature presents us with elements of irreducible chance, we shall find this appeal for a new logic unnecessary - without implying that all is well and that all conceptual problems are solved or even seen.

We have a screen with two apertures. On one side we have an excited atom S which can lose a light quantum. The detectors are placed at various points in a plane B. The physical process we are interested in is that in which the initially excited source loses energy and the detector gains energy. We wish to find the transition probability from the initial state (in which no photon is present), to the final state (in which no photon is present), as it depends on the position of the second atom in the plane B. This is a clear problem of quantum electrodynamics in which two atoms change their state and in the process a photon is created and destroyed.

The two-slit problem is therefore well defined and does not require us to study a photon in its flight from source to detector. The solution shows that the probability of transition depends on the· position of the detector in conformity with the results of classical optics - as could be expected. But it gives only probabilities. Again, the continuum is the birthplace of chance.

Now, what has happened to the 'mystery'? Are we not faced with a situation very much like that of Newton when he worried about the cause of gravitation? He could calculate the acceleration of bodies, given their position in space. The bodies interacted only through the gravitational field. As we know, Newton did not find the cause of gravitation, and physicists found they could get on very well without having explained gravitation. The movement of bodies under the influence of gravitation is according to law. The transfer of excitation in the presence of the electromagnetic field has an element of chance: this is the difference.

In spite of the evidence discussed, the acceptance of chance as an element of nature has not been easy; leaders of modern physics explored other or supplementary avenues of interpretation. Bohr and Heisenberg early suggested that quantum mechanics reveals in atomic processes not only the complementarity of particles and waves, but also a feature of wholeness quite foreign to the mechanical conception of nature. It is, so it was argued, a particular weakness of this conception that it is based on the complete detachment of the subject of research from its object.

Now, if the historical and logical survey presented here has any significance, this complete detachment is the cornerstone of scientific thought and cannot be abandoned without imperilling the whole structure. How could it ever come under attack?

Jammer, the historian of quantum theory, has told us that Bohr was a friend and spiritual disciple of the Danish philosopher *Höffding, (1843-1931)* who is best known through his History of Modern Philosophy. Höffding was also one of the first to recognise the philosophical importance of *Kierkegaard, (1813-1855)* a Danish philosopher of the first half of the 19th century. Kierkegaard's approach has been summarised as follows:

> 'What Plato had accomplished for the objective consciousness with the concept of the *idea*, Kierkegaard did for subjectivity with the concept of *existence*... All philosophy looks towards a totality of Being, but all object being is not yet the totality of being. The object is just one side of it. The insight that objects are there only for a subject makes possible, at times, a return to the subject. But the subject withdraws from customary thinking'. (Knaus 1957).

Kierkegaard also taught that the life of the individual proceeds from state to state, each state being established by a breach of continuity.

Such lessons may well have influenced Bohr in his extending the idea of complementarity to include the relation between the subject - taken as the observer - and the object - the atom.

Kierkegaard's contribution to philosophical thought was given prominence by Bohr's contemporary *Karl Jaspers (1883-1969)*.

Jaspers proceeded from the 'concept' of 'Existenz' to that of the 'encompassing' - (Das Umgreifende): 'In order to get into the realms of origin a type of thinking has to be performed which seems impossible. We think in objects which we intend. The fundamental philosophical operation at all times is ... to transcend towards that out of which the objective arises. What is neither subject nor act of thinking (subject) but contains both within itself, I have called the Encompassing ... If we call objectified thinking rational, then any thinking which, guided by the objective, goes beyond this, is itself no longer rational although at each stage bound to rational acts (Jaspers 1957).'

But whereas Jaspers insisted that the sciences must remain objective and capable of objective communication -

they pay for this by their failure to achieve a total system of Being of the world, because objective being is not Being as such.

- Bohr and Heisenberg came close to postulating, as implied in the formalism of quantum mechanics and necessary for the interpretation of quantum phenomena, an idea of *wholeness* which encompasses subject and object, and finds its expression in the simultaneous use of logically contradictory concepts. By itself, the simultaneous use of a particle model and a wave model to describe the result of experiment need not imply more than the absence of a macroscopic analogue of the phenomenon observed.

Heisenberg (1969) has recently published a book of memoirs, an account of discussions he has had concerning atomic physics. To this he gave the title Der Teil und das Ganze (The Part and the Whole) - alluding to his conviction that in the new theories, to the creation of which he contributed so much, all parts are so tied to the whole that they cannot be entirely separated. He recalls some remarks made in 1927 by Niels Bohr, which indicate that at that time he accepted the distinction between philosophical and scientific thinking on which Jaspers had insisted. But five years later Bohr spoke of the physical notion of complementarity 'serving to symbolise the fundamental limitations of the objective existence of phenomena independent of the means of their observation' (Bohr 1933). Then: 'For a parallel to the lessons of atomic theory regarding the limited applicability of the discrimination between the behaviour of material objects and the question of their observation we must in fact turn to quite other branches of science, such as psychology, or even to that kind of epistemological problem with which already thinkers like Buddha and Lao Tse have been confronted, when trying to harmonise our position as spectators and actors in the great drama of existence' (Bohr 1937). And 'Planck's discovery of the universal quantum of action revealed in atomic processes a feature of wholeness quite foreign to the mechanical conception of nature' (Bohr 1954). 'The interaction between the objects and the measuring instruments forms an integral part of the phenomenon. The essential wholeness of a proper quantum phenomenon finds indeed logical expression in the circumstances that any attempt at its subdivision would require a change in the experimental arrangement incompatible with the appearance of the phenomenon itself.' (Bohr 1954).

Neither Bohr nor Heisenberg however left any doubt that their appeal to wholeness would not imply a return to complete necessity. But if chance is invoked in any case, such an appeal to wholeness is barely justified.

The idea of wholeness has been taken up by Bohm and his collaborators, in an attempt to basically re-formulate quantum mechanics. They draw particular attention to certain features of the wave function of many particle systems which indicate an interdependence of spatially separated particles such as is not found in classical physics. This, they say, as well as the observer-observed relation, goes to show that in quantum physics all parts depend on the whole, and the more of the universe that is taken into account, the more will the information be complete. But again, that the appeal to wholeness does not provide an escape from the aleatory character of the physical world is almost agreed to. 'It is clear that the incompleteness of content of a theory is necessary for wholeness in form. A theory that is whole in form may be compared with a seed that can grow in an indefinite number of ways' (Bohm and Hiley 1975). - Anything can happen, obviously, in remote parts of the whole.

Theoretical physics such as developed in the last few centuries saw no case to answer when confronted with the *existential* situation of chance. It could not, however, escape the evidence offered by the experimenters. How it responded to this evidence has now been indicated. A system of concepts has been developed which, whilst exhausting the sources of information available, implies, and at the same time hides, the occurrence in nature of absolute chance.

The 'law of large numbers' is often called upon to account for the transition from elementary randomness to the regularity of the practical world. It has been recognised (Borel, Planck, Exner) that lawfulness on a large scale is compatible with randomness in elementary events. Large numbers by themselves do not, of course, create order out of chaos. They only guarantee that the observed averages reflect the probabilities inherent in the individual events. Gases for instance satisfy well-defined laws because all constituent molecules have the same probabilities for location and for momentum. Or, the absent minded wanderer who every few minutes forgets from which direction he came, will after a few hours find the starting point his most probable location, because any other particular place is less likely. An observer who plots the journey of thousands of such wanderers (the ensemble) will observe the highest density of endpoints at the origin. In spite of this, the individual wanderer is likely not to return to where he started from. The law of large numbers does not apply to individual cases. It is relevant only where averages over large numbers of individual cases are of interest. But frequently it is precisely the individual case which matters.

A logical operation, however lengthy and involved it may be, is wrecked by a single false step in the reasoning. The nearest material analogue to reasoning is electronic computation. This operates at any stage with the choice of alternatives and, except for a few built-in redundancies, the result depends absolutely on each step, as random errors do not average out.

A second field in which the law of large numbers appears to fail is that of genetics. This was recently put forward in an impressive manner by Monod (1970). Monod contends that the biosphere does not contain a predictable class of objects; its beginning constitutes a particular event, compatible with first principles but not deducible from them. The further development of life is no less a matter of chance than its origin. True, a cell normally operates as a machine, but alterations or mutations take place by chance. Chance is the only possible source of modification in the genetic text, of any novelty or creation. Chance is effective here because a mutation is a sub-microscopic event, involving primarily single quanta. One separate mutation is, however, still reversible. The reversibility disappears when a sufficiently large number of mutations co-operate, providing a viable variation in the pattern of living matter. 'The elementary events are random, but once laid down, enter the reign of necessity. Natural selection is based on the products of chance.'

If chance has acted in the development of the biosphere, it must also be active in the normal functioning of the living body and can be expected to lead to its most significant effects in the functioning of the human brain. Today's version of the alternative to necessity which Epicurus had postulated, allows us to speculate how decisions and deliberations *utilise* (but do not constitute!) the forking of the causality of elementary events, how morally and logically a chance of alternative sequence can become significant in allowing us to will yes or no, to give way or to 'stand up to temptation'. In the hostelry of life we are offered a limited menu; our deliberate choice is pure chance for the cook. This is one side of our interest in chance. The other one was superbly expressed by Dewey:

> 'Man finds himself living in an aleatory world; his existence involves, to put it baldly, a gamble. The world is a scene of risk, it is uncertain, unstable, uncannily unstable. Its dangers are irregular, inconstant, not to be counted upon as to their times and seasons...'.

Appendix A
Burgersdijk's Classification of Causes

The classification of causes, suggested in some of Plato's dialogues, systematically explored by Aristotle, became an important object of logical studies. Duns Scotus' ideas, outlined above, provide a significant example. Such studies probably reached a summit in Franco Burgersdijk's (1590-1629) *Institutionum Logicarum Libri Duo*. Burgersdijk's table of causes is an extension and elaboration of Aristotle's classification (Table 1).

Wolf (1910), in the comments to his translation of Spinoza's *Short Treatise,* has summarised Burgersdijk's explanations of the efficient causes as follows:

'An *emanative* cause is one which produces its effect by its sheer existence, while an *active* cause, or *acting* cause, is one which produces its effect through the medium of some activity which it exercises. Fire, for instance, is the *emanative* cause of its own heat, but an *active* cause of the heat which it imparts to other things. Spinoza practically does away with this distinction in the case of God.

An *immanent* cause is a cause whose effects are confined within itself, as distinguished from a *transeunt* cause which operates on things outside itself. God, according to Spinoza is an immanent cause for the same reason that he is *causa sui*, namely, because 'outside God there is nothing at all', whether to affect him or to be affected by him. In other words, Spinoza's God is not a *transcendent* but an *immanent* god.

A *free* cause is one which acts from deliberate choice; a *natural* (or *necessary*) cause is one which acts from necessity (*causa libera est, quae consulto - id est, ex judicio rationis - causat. Causa libera potest agere, aut non agere, quid quid, quantum et quando lubet. Necessaria, quae non consulto, sed necessitate naturae causat. Causa necessaria ad unum aliquod agendum determinata est, agitque quando et quantum potest.*) This distinction, however, did not commend itself to Spinoza. He employed these antithetic terms somewhat differently. By a free cause he meant one which acts wihout any *external* compulsion, or externally imposed necessity. In this sense a cause might be *free* although acting from necessity, namely, when the necessity was inherent in its own character, and not due to outside forces.

Burgersdijk's Classification of Causes

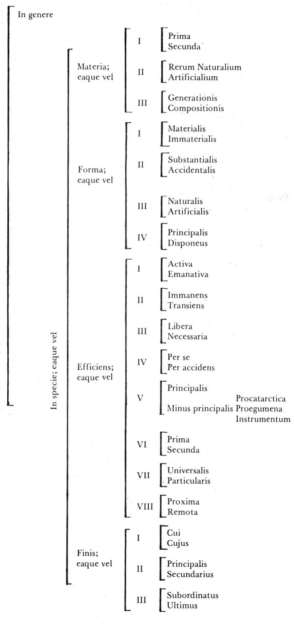

Table I

A cause *through himself*, or *causa per se*, is one whose effects are due to his or its own natural character; a *cause per accidens* is one which produces a certain effect not as the result of its own character, but owing to some unusual circumstances. If, for instance, an animal gives birth to one of its own kind it is a *causa per se*, but if it gives birth to a monstrosity, then it is a *causa per accidens*.

A *principal* cause is one which produces an effect by virtue of its own powers alone, without the aid of anything else. A subsidiary cause *(causa minus principalis)* is merely one condition or factor which is necessary but not adequate to produce a certain effect. Three kinds of *subsidiary* causes were recognised. Almost any means employed in the production of an effect was called an *instrumental* cause. A second species of subsidiary cause is the *provoking* or *inciting* cause *(causa procatarctica vel causa incipiens aut inchoans)* - that is any external thing or condition which incites the *principal* cause to action. The third kind of subsidiary cause is the *predisposing* cause *(causa proegumena)* or some internal condition which predisposes a thing towards a certain kind of action or process.

A *first* cause is one which is not dependent on (or the effect of) any other cause; a *causa secunda* is dependent on a first cause.

A *universal* cause was contrasted with a particular one as follows. The latter can only produce one kind of effect; the former can produce different kinds of effect by co-operating with various other causes. *(Causa universalis est, quae eadem efficientia cum aliis causis concurrit ad plura effecta; causa particularis est, quae sua efficientia unum tantum effectum producit)*. God, according to Spinoza, is an *universal* cause in so far as he is not restricted to any one kind of effect, but not in the sense that he can co-operate with causes outside him.

A *proximate* cause produces its effect immediately, without the intervention of anything else, while the *remote* cause produces its effect by means of an intervening proximate cause or chain of proximate causes. The terms *proximate* and *remote* are relative to a given effect; every cause might be both proximate and remote, but not in relation to the same effect.

No doubt, classifications such as those given by Burgersdijk can throw light on the meaning of the cause-effect relation. They must also assist in dispelling the idea that by adding a large number of causes a *complete* history of an event can be given, or even a closed system of the world can be constructed.

Appendix B
Interpreters of the New Physics

With the quantum era a new situation was created as far as causality and chance were concerned. In chapter 7 I have given an account of the emerging implications for thought on these subjects of the new way of looking at phenomena. It may be of interest to the reader on the one hand to see to what extent these notions have become the recognised creed of atomic scientists, and have been expounded in print, and, on the other hand, to get an idea of alternative interpretations including some suggested by, perhaps, insufficiently erudite authors. What I have learned from previous publications has, of course, been incorporated in my account.

I have therefore collected in this appendix a series of abstracts of relevant writings, and trust that the reader will have no difficulties in tracing the relation between the analysis presented here and earlier interpretations.

There was the Viennese school with its extreme positivistic views. *Philipp Frank (1932)* identified both physics and personal experience with reality.

He came to the conclusion that the question of strict causality in nature is senseless, except from the standpoint of school-philosophers. Laws of causality have far less to say about the real world than is 'usually thought'. True propositions are either tautological or specific for a particular element of reality, such as the proposition that the table is blue. The so-called law of causality, stating that everything is determined in advance, is at best a tautology because things happen only in one way. Laplace's world formula has meaning only for a fictitious super-human intelligence, but even this cannot cope with the electromagnetic continuum. Frank holds that it is finally vanquished by the consideration that the precision of any measurement is limited. Accidental, on the other hand, is an event which cannot be foreseen by means of the relevant law of causality. 'The concept of lawlessness cannot be expressed as a proposition about personal experience.'

Similar ideas were expressed by *M. Schlick* in 1931. In particular, Schlick castigates Bohr for relating indeterminism to free will. This, he states, is metaphysical nonsense. There is nothing in any case to be said for a principle stating that *everything* is determined by laws, although laws may exist which enable man to forecast *some* elements of the future. It is useless to say that quantum ideas violate the principle of causality because causality is only an exhortation to look for a connexion which may or may not exist. In a later essay Schlick concludes that the only justification for talking of causality, i.e. of *propter hoc* as against *post hoc,* is a regularity or uniformity of sequence. As regularity is established by a limited number of cases, it is always open to doubt, but failures in regularity can also be interpreted as due to intervening circumstances. These should be minimised by filling spatial and temporal gaps in the contiguity of events. But this is all. No additional 'glue' can be found, as was clearly seen by Hume. In science in particular, the principle of causality can be regarded as a statement that there is order in nature, that all events in nature are subject to laws, i.e. to mathematical formulae or equations, according to which things happen. Determinism means the possibility of their calculation and nothing else. For very small particles accurate prediction is impossible, but for ordinary purposes the deterministic attitude remains justified and is the only one compatible with our knowledge of nature. If h were much bigger, nothing could be planned, engineering as well as reality and all human existence would have to be given up.

Popper (1959) formulates the principle of causality as follows:

'The principle of causality is the assertion that any event whatsoever can be causally explained, that it can be deductively predicted'. But the belief in causality is metaphysical and hence futile. On the other hand, a statement free from metaphysical elements can have indeterministic conclusions only if these are falsifiable. The search for laws and prediction cannot be abandoned without repudiating the empirical character of hypotheses. It is as self-contradictory to think that an empirical hypothesis could exist which might compel us to abandon the search for laws, as it is to give a causal explanation why causal explanation is impossible, i.e. that causality breaks down because of causal interaction with the observed object: this was Heisenberg's idea. Popper thinks that the sciences are systems of theories, and that it is feasible to disprove, but not to verify a theory.

Carnap (1966) who also stems from the Viennese circle identifies causal relations with potential predictability, given the whole previous situation, i.e. all the relevant facts and all the relevant laws of nature.

There is no point in talking of 'necessity'. 'When it is said for example, that iron expands when heated, nothing more is meant than that one event follows the other. The words 'necessity' and 'must' add nothing significant to laws. This position was taken by Hume.'

A physicist may comment that for him the thermal expansion of iron means something different from and a great deal more than, one event following the other and that this extra does add significance to the relation.

In a collection of essays, edited by *H. Feigl* and *M. Brodbeck* (1953), chapter 5 deals with causality, determinism and probability, with contributions by Russell, Feigl, Nagel and Bergmann.

Bertrand Russell emphasises that the word 'cause' is bound up with misleading associations and he discusses a few ambiguities in the common usage.

Russell is essentially determinist. Uniformity in nature has to be assumed, spatially and temporally. The 'law of causality' will be replaced by reference to special, frequently observed sequences and in physics, by differential equations which are symmetrical with respect to past and future. The equations are verifiable if the course of events is approximately the same in two states of the universe. What can be inferred and what is in fact determined are often confused. The past is determined by the fact that it has happened. It is known by causal inferences and memory. The future is determined by the fact that it will happen, but it is known by inference only; the past would have been different if our present wishes had been different because these are conditioned by the past. Our present wishes cannot be different from what they are now.

Are human actions predictable? *Bergson* says no because every event presents genuine novelty, it embodies too much of the past to be a repetition. But there is sufficient repetition for laws to hold. It is most likely that all human volitions are subject to causal laws but these do not compel a man to do what he would rather not do. That man subjectively senses freedom in deliberation does not prove that the result of the deliberation is a free choice and does not disprove that volitions have causes; causes are not analogous to volition, and an outside cause is not analogous to an alien will. The idea of the indeterminism of future events is merely the result of ignorance. Mere ignorance cannot be an essential feature of any desirable kind of free will. Freedom in any valuable sense demands only that our volitions shall be the result of our own desires, not of outside force compelling us to will what we would rather not will.

Feigl (see also Feigl & Sellars, 1949) is terrified of *'metaphysical bondage'*.

He contrasts the *'purified concept of causation'*, defined as predictability according to law or to a set of laws, or defined alternatively as functional relation with testable features, on the one hand and, on the other hand, *cause-effect relations, intrinsic necessity* and other *disturbing connotations* such as animistic conceptions or rules of logical reasoning. Laws can be of the deterministic or of the statistical type, they can be qualitative, semi-quantitative or fully quantitative. The *domain of their application* is either temporal succession or sequential or co-existential features. The cause-effect relation implies temporal irreversible succession. Macro-processes of everyday life are irreversible, but this irreversibility is compatible with reversibility of molecular processes. Determinism equals complete predictability, but even classical physics knows of unsurmountable limitations to the exactness of measurements. The vividly debated consequences of the limits set by quantum theory to predictability, Feigl comments, are precisely nil for the simple reason that the free will problem is a pseudo-issue arising out of confusion of meanings; not determination but compulsion is the opposite of freedom.

Ernest Nagel discussing the causal character of modern physical theory, contrasts the classical and the quantum points of view.

The classical assumption is that events of nature occur in causal orders. They are controlled by differential equations not containing time explicitly and requiring constants of integration. Classical mechanics has its restrictions. It is concerned with a limited set of properties. Extended so as to include fields, it remains deterministic, though (a) no experimental values are ever exact and (b) instantaneous values may be misleading on account of hysteresis effects. It is therefore necessary to distinguish between logical structure and observational relevance.

In quantum theory the uncertainty relation is held to mark its indeterministic character. But it may be improper to describe electrons in terms of particles and waves or the state of any system in terms of position and momentum; a system cannot be expected to be deterministic with respect to a wrong description of it. Quantum mechanics is after all deterministic with respect to the quantum mechanical description of state, but even if the sub-atomic processes were a-causal and statistical, the resultant macro-processes and macro-states would still be causal.

Finally, a sentence from *Gustav Bergmann's* contribution may be quoted.

'Our observing makes no difference to the behaviour of ordinary physical objects. This behaviour is the subject matter of all measurements, all science. A radical notion of subjectivity cannot enter into the methodological analysis of science'.

Silberstein (1933), taking causality as a maxim based on the uniformity of nature, tends towards a deterministic view: he does not discriminate between the principle of determinism and that of causality.

Equal causes have equal effects, but in fragments of nature, which alone can be tested, only approximately equal conditions can be expected, while it must be doubted that the whole universe ever returns to the same state. Also in a detailed study such as the cooling of a sphere, or the history of a star, the initial state is not studied as the effect of a previous state as its cause, so that in practice the chain of causes cannot be traced back indefinitely by a particular law. Two incomplete systems can always be combined into one complete system. If a system is incomplete, we search for a second system which, interacting with the first, completes, it. In this way the principle of causality gained credence. But we have no authority to consider the whole universe as a complete undisturbed system.

The principle is now being undermined, but a maxim is neither true nor false. Denial of determinism simply amounts to closing the enquiry. Do we really know enough about atoms and elementary particles? Is modern quantum theory for ever? The need for specifying the apparatus is not really new. It simply means enlarging the system considered so as to include it.

A graphical representation of indeterminacy would show bifurcation or polyfurcation, different routes for different realisations of identical conditions (remember here Simmels' individual causality, page 46) - can we consider these as sources of free will? Silberstein says no: 'But a moment's introspection into a few actual instances of one's own 'free will' exertion will convince everybody of the emptiness of such speculation'.

The reader may be reminded that, above, a different view was advocated of the connexion between free will and 'forked' causality; though it must be agreed that introspection will not assist in elucidating the relation.

Extensive discussions of the post-quantum ideas of causality have been given by Blokhintsev, Bohm, Born, Bunge, Cassirer, Margenau, von Weizsäcker. Of these, the first three are physicists' accounts, the following two philosophers' accounts, von Weizsäcker and Margenau stand in the middle.

Cassirer (1956) is a Neo-Kantian. He criticises Laplace and du Bois-Reymond with him for mistaking the symbols created by the human mind for mysterious truth.

The question of causality is not about things but about knowledge. In classical physics the level of knowledge rises from measurements via laws to principles. The principle of causality is not a natural law amongst others; it is not an insight but rather a postulate concerning a method of structuring experience. Cassirer considers chance only in one of the Aristotelian senses, namely as opposed to essence. Quantum theory does not essentially affect the interpretation of the critically interpreted causal law, because the attack is not levelled against the laws as such - nature is nothing but an aggregate of laws, which constitute the objects rather than their being derived from them. The novelty of quantum mechanics refers to the relation of thing and attribute. Classically the state of a thing is at a given moment completely determined with respect to all possible attributes. But what is meant by state depends on the language used.

Cassirer asserts that the problems of ethics and free will are not related to those of causality or causelessness: freedom does not need to be upheld against physical causality.

M. Bunge (1959) is interested in elucidating the concept of causality as a clue to the way the world runs. His sources are common usage of the term and scientific practice.

Bunge takes causality to be a species of the general concept of determination, with a number of specific properties. But predictability is a criterion of the validity of nomological hypotheses about the time sequences, whereas causality belongs to objects, not to the knowledge of objects. Causality is an ontological relation, i.e. a property of objective events. Causality is asymmetric, i.e. cause and effect cannot be exchanged. It always relates to distinct events as a unique one-to-one relation, but as a first approximation different causes can act simultaneously without interfering with each other. The cause has efficacy in producing, or assisting in producing, the effect and does not just precede it. And finally, the cause acts externally; it does something which the effect partner would not do by itself, e.g. by way of inertia. But extrinsic causes do not always take a 'grip' on the proper nature and the inner processes of things, hence comes self-determination on every level such as inertia, germination, freedom. The aim of the sciences is the establishment of laws, but not all laws are causal.

Strict and pure causation never explains anything completely. Causal hypotheses are no more and no less than rough, approximate reconstructions, but they are indispensable and sometimes adequate. A particular process can, for example, be interactive initially, then causal, then self-determined.

M. Born in his lectures on the Natural Philosophy of Cause and Chance (Oxford 1949) presents a selection of topics from theoretical physics with a view to illustrating his ideas of cause and chance.

Nature is ruled by the laws of causation and the laws of chance in a certain admixture. How is this possible? Real things depend on each other, as is inferred from observation, through relations involving or not involving time. Determinism means the connection of events at different times so as to permit prediction. Causality postulates laws of dependence. Pre-Newtonian astronomy, for example, was deterministic but not causal. As rules of observation include rules of errors, the conception of chance, more fundamental than causality, enters early into scientific activity. The introduction of chance (or the explicit introduction of ignorance) removes reversibility and thus leads to direction of time. The formalism of quantum mechanics came before its interpretation involving chance. Dynamic problems in quantum mechanics cannot be defined before the subject has decided in which aspect of the development he is interested. Quantum mechanics does not describe a situation in an objective external world but a definite experimental arrangement for observing a section of it. It does not eliminate causality, but rather its identification with determinism. Born's book is based on a superb command of theoretical physics, it is full of thought-provoking remarks.

D. I. Blokhintsev (1965/68) takes a radically probabilistic view:

We cannot ignore the element of games of chance in the behaviour of the universe: God has a penchant for games of chance. The basic assumption of classical mechanics that it is possible to determine the future is based on an abstraction. Statistical laws cannot be deduced from deterministic ones.

Quantum mechanics provides a symphony of new statistical laws. They differ from those of classical statistical mechanics which refer to a phase-space in which position and movements are equivalent co-ordinates. In quantum mechanics there is no ensemble in which both groups of variables have definite values. Bohr formulated this result differently, viz. as the principle of complementarity, reflecting his philosophical concepts.

Blokhintsev believes in the reality of particles, but accepts the wave function as indispensable. Individual particles are not subject to causal laws so that their history can be traced only in very general terms. The wave function describes an objective feature of nature.

This information which quantum mechanics gives is incomplete. From this it may or may not be concluded that latent hidden parameters *exist* which, if available, would complete the information. But only if such parameters are in principle unobservable would their existence not be in conflict with the principle of complementarity.

Blokhintsev's highly competent analysis is addressed in the first instance to advanced students of theoretical physics. His close and precise reasoning reflects probably best what may be called the majority view in physics.

For *Bohm (1957)* the laws of nature include causal laws, laws of chance and laws dealing with the relationship between causality and chance.

We interpret constancy as signifying necessary relationships termed causal laws. There are one-to-many and many-to-one and many-to-many causal relationships. Statistical laws are approximate causal laws that apply to large aggregates. Considering causal laws, we find that one obtains level after level of approximation each involving qualitatively different kinds of causal factors. This 'level after level' idea is the main burden of Bohm's book. It is discussed with reference to classical physics and quantum physics in turn. Let us assume that the world as a whole is real and has a precisely describable and analysable structure of unlimited complexity; the idea of level then suggests first, a sub-quantum mechancial level containing hidden variables, and beyond this an infinity, a depth inexhaustible in the proportion and qualities of matter-levels within levels. The basic reality is the totality of actually existing matter in the process of becoming; it can be represented only with the aid of an inexhaustable series of abstractions.

Weizsäcker (1952) is satisfied that the physical view of the world does not embrace all the essential properties of things.

The wholeness of living things requires emotional, historical, religious values. In the physical world waves and particles are ultimate concepts, but atoms fit neither alone; we cannot have any experience of atoms except through experiment, and the experiment is a violation of nature. Subjectivity plays a major part in physics. The cause-effect relation as asymmetric in time is really foreign to modern physics. It implies and is based on human action, i.e. the freedom to choose experimental conditions at will. The relation is maintained in quantum theory, although the principle of determinism is relaxed together with the concept of objects which exist by themselves quite independent of the observing subject.

Margenau's (1950) point of departure is the analysis of experience.

What is immediately given is not, or not yet, experience, nor is the spectator-spectacle duality immediately obvious. Only experience can provide a stable basis for an objective world. The transition from sensory fact to reason is gradual. Things, external objects, laws ... are constructs connected by rules of correspondence with one's immediate perception. The constructs, to be accepted as valid, must satisfy certain requirements, of which causality is one: in the sense of a relation between constructs, in particular between states of physical systems, by which a given state of a physical system is invariably followed by another specifiable state. Causality is thus not a relation between immediately perceived phenomena. It is a metaphysical requirement which demands that constructs must be chosen so as to generate causal laws. Margenau then distinguishes between partial causes such as the Aristotelian causes, and total causes which are the entire state of affairs preceding the effect. Only total causes are unique, referring to physical systems assumed to be closed.

Margenau proceeds to identify causality with the validity of laws, in particular laws in the form of differential equations which relate successive stages of the same continuous process. 'Causality holds if the laws of nature governing closed systems do not contain the time variable in explicit terms.' If they do, the laws themselves would change in an unaccountable manner.

The changes which quantum theory has introduced do not refer to causality but to what defines the state of a system. Quantum mechanics remains committed to the principle of causality; in classical physics the state of a system, say of a molecule, is given by properties which are *possessed* by the system, i.e. properties which the system has continuously and which it yields whenever it is seen. The properties of quantum systems, on the contrary, are *latent*. The process of searching for the electron combines with the wave function to prepare the state which enables the electron to appear as a point particle. Latent observables can have different values in different observations, but have sufficient stability to produce, on repeated measurements, (on one system, or equal systems prepared in the same way) a set of values with a definite statistical distribution. It is to these distributions that the laws of quantum theory and hence strict causality applies.

There is no reference to chance in Margenau's treatise.

105

References

AGRICOLA, G. *De Re Metallica (1556)* Dover Publications Inc., New York, 1950.

ARISTOTLE. *The Physics I, II*
The Metaphysics
Posterior Analytics
The Loeb Classical Library. William Heinemann Ltd., London, and Harvard University Press, Cambridge, Mass.

AUGER, P., BORN, M., HEISENBERG, W., SCHRÖDINGER, E. *On Modern Physics.* Clarkson N. Potter, Inc., New York, 1961.

BERNAL, J.D. *Aspects of Dialectical Materialism.* Watts, 1934. Reprinted in *The Freedom of Necessity.* Routledge & Kegan Paul, London, 1949.

BLOKHINTSEV, D.I. *The Philosophy of Quantum Mechancis. (1965)* D. Reidel Publishing Co., Dordrecht, 1968.

BOETIUS. *The Consolation of Philosophy.* The Penguin Classics, 1969.

BOHM, D.J. *Causality and Chance in Modern Physics.* Routledge & Kegan Paul, London, 1957.

BOHM, D.J., HILEY, B. *On the Intuitive Understanding of Non-Locality as Implied by Quantum Theory. Foundations of Physics* 5, 93. 1975.

BOHR, N. *Das Quanten-postulat. Naturw.* 16, *245,* 1928.

BOHR, N. *Atomic Physics and Human Knowledge.* Chapman and Hall, London, 1958.

Du BOIS-REYMOND, E. *Reden, Erste Folge.* Leipzig, 1886

BOREL, E. *Le Hasard.* (1914). Librairie Felix Alcan, Paris, 1928.

BORN, M. *Quantenmechanik der Stossvorgänge. Z. Physik* 38, 803, 1926.

BORN, M. *Das Adiabatenprinzip in der Quantenmechanik. Z. Physik* 40, 167, 1927.

BORN, M. *Natural Philosophy of Cause and Chance.* Clarendon Press, Oxford, 1949.

BRUNSCHVICG, L. *L'Experience Humaine et la Causalité Physique (1922).* Presses Universitaires de France, Paris, 1949.

BUNGE, M. *Causality.* Harvard University Press, Cambridge, Mass and Oxford University Press, 1959.

BURGERSDIJK, F. = *Burgersdicii, Fr. Institutiorum Logicarum Libri Duo.* Cantabrigiae, 1660.

CAMPBELL, C.A. *In Defence of Free Will.* George Allen and Unwin Ltd., London 1967.

CARNAP, R. *Philosophical Foundation of Physics.* Basic Books Inc., New York and London, 1966.

CASSIRER, E. *The Philosophy of Symbolic Forms.* Yale University Press, New Haven, 1935.

CASSIRER, E. *Determinism and Indeterminism in Modern Physics.* Yale University Press, New Haven, 1956.

CHAITIN, G.J. *Randomness and Mathematical Proof.* Scientific American, May 1975.

CICERO. *De Natura Deorum.* Loeb Classical Library. 1933 *De Fato.* Loeb Classical Lebrary, 1948.

COOLIDGE, J.L. *An Introduction to Mathematical Probability.* Oxford University Press, 1925.

COPLESTON, F.C. *A History of Philosophy, Vol. II. Mediaeval Philosophy.* Methuen & Co. Ltd., London, 1972.

DEWEY, J. *Experience and Nature (1929).* Dover Publications Inc., New York, 1958.

DEWEY, J. *On Experience, Nature and Freedom.* ed. R.J. Bernstein. The Bobbs-Messil Co. Inc., Indianapolis - New York, 1960.

DIOGENES LAERTIUS. *Vol. II.* The Loeb Classical Library, 1925.

DUHEM, P. *Essai Sur la Notion de Théorie physique de Platon à Galilee.* Harmann et Fils, Paris 1908.

EDDINGTON, A.S. *The Nature of the Physical World.* Cambridge University Press 1928.

EINSTEIN, A. *Philosopher-Scientist.* ed. P.A. Schilp (1949). Harper Torchbook edition, 1959.

EINSTEIN, A. and BORN, M. *Briefwechsel 1916-1955.* Nymphenburger Verlagshandlung, München, 1969.

ENGELS, F. *Dialectics of Nature.* Lawrence and Wishart, London, 1940.

EXNER, F. *Vorlesungen über die physikalischen Grundlagen der Naturwissenschaften.* Wien, 1919.

EWING, A.C. *Kant's Treatment of Causality.* Kegan Paul, London 1924.

FEIGL, H., BRODBECK, M. *Readings in the Philosoph'y of Science.* Appleton-Century-Crofts, Inc., New York, 1953.

FEIGL, H., SELLARS, W. *Readings in Philosophical Analysis.* Appleton-Century-Crofts, Inc., New York, 1949.

FEYNMAN, R.P. *Lectures on Physics: Quantum Mechanics.* Addison-Wesley Publishing Co. Inc., Reading, Mass. 1965.

FRANK, P. *Das Kausalgesetz und seine Grenzen.* Julius Springer, Wien, 1932.

HEISENBERG, W. *The Physical Principles of the Quantum Theory.* Dover Publications, Inc., New York, 1950.

HEISENBERG, W. *Der Teil und das Ganze.* R. Piper & Co., München, 1969.

HÖFFDING, H. *A History of Modern Philosophy.* Macmillan & Co., London, 1900.

HÖFFDING, H. *Soren Kierkegaard als Philosoph.* Fr. Frommann, Stuttgart, 1902.

HUME, D. *A Treatise on Human Nature.* Longmans, Green & Co., London 1874.

HUME, D. *An Enquiry concerning Human Understanding. Selection from Treatise.* Claredon Press, Oxford 1894 and 1902.

JAMES, W. *The Will to Belief, and other Essays.* Longmann, Green & Co., London 1897.

JAMMER, M. *The Conceptual Development of Quantum Mechanics.* McGraw-Hill Book Company Inc., New York, 1966.

JASPERS, K. *The Philosophy of Karl Jaspers* ed. P.A. Schilp. (includes G. Knaus, *The Concept of the Encompassing*). Tudor Publishing Co., New York, 1957.

KANT, I. *Kritik der Reinen Vernunft.* Hartknoch, Riga, 1781.

KELSEN, H. *Society and Nature.* The University of Chicago Press, 1943.

KEPLER, J. *De Stella Nova in Pede Serpantarii.* Prag, 1606.

KNAUS, G. see Jaspers, 1957.

LERNER, D. (ed) *Cause and Effect. The Hayden Colloquium on Scientific Method and Concept.* The Free Press, New York, 1965.

LUCRETIUS. *De Rerum Natura.* The Loeb Classical Library, 1966.

MARGENAU, H. *The Nature of Physical Reality.* McGraw-Hill Book Company Inc., New York, 1950.

MARX, K. Dissertation: *Über die Differenz der Demokritischen und Epikureischen Naturphilosophie (1891). Frühe Schriften, Vol. I,* J.G. Cotta, Stuttgart, 1962.

MAUND, C. *Hume's Theory of Knowledge.* Macmillan & Co., London, 1937.

MONOD, J. *Le Hasard et la Nécessité.* Paris, 1970. translated by A. Wainhouse, Collins, London, 1972.

NEWTON, I. *Philosophiae Naturalis Principia Mathematica.* Reprinted by Maclehose, Glasgow, 1871.

PEIRCE, C.S. *Selected Writings.* Ed. P.P. Wiener. University Press, Stanford, 1958.

PLANCK, M. *Wege zur Physikalischen Erkenntnis.* Leipzig, 1933.

PLANCK, M. *Scientific Autobiography and other Papers.* Williams and Norgate, London, 1950.

PLATO. *Phaedo. The Last Days of Socrates.* Penguin Classics. Harmondsworth, 1969.

PLUZANSKI, E. *Essai sur la Philosophie de Duns Scot.* Paris, 1887.

POINCARÉ, H. *Science and Hypotheses.* Walter Scott Publishing Co., London, 1905.

POPPER, K.R. *The Logic of Scientific Discovery.* Hutchinson, London, 1959.

REICHENBACH, M. *Philosophic Foundations of Quantum Mechanics.* University of California Press, Berkeley and Los Angeles, 1944.

REICHENBACH, M. *The Theory of Relativity and A Priori Knowledge.* (1920). Universtiy of California Press, Berkeley and Los Angeles, 1965.

RENNINGER, M. *Z. Physik* 158, *413, 1960.*

RICKERT, H. *Die Grenzen der Naturwissenschaftlichen Begriffsbildung* (1902). J.C.B. Mohr, Tübingen, 1921.

ROSS, W.D. *Aristotle (1923).* Methuen & Co. Ltd., London, 1949.

SCHLICK, M. *Naturwissenschaften* 19, *145, 1931.*

SCHOPENHAUER, A. *Satz vom Grunde.* Sämtliche Werke, Brockhaus, Leipzig, 1877.

SILBERSTEIN, L. *Causality.* Macmillan & Co., London, 1933.

SIMMEL, G. *Die Probleme der Geschichtsphilosophie.* Duncker & Humblot, München und Leipzig, 1907.

SULLIVAN, J.W.N. *Contemporary Mind.* Humphrey Toulmin, London, 1934.

TALMUD, *The Living Talmud. Selected Mentor Religious Classics.* New American Library, New York, 1957.

TATON, R. (Ed.) *A General History of the Sciences.* (4 Vols.) Thames and Hudson, London 1963/6.

TODHUNTER, I. *A History of the Mathematical Theory of Probability.* (1865) Macmillan & Co., London, Stechert, New York, 1931.

TISZA, L. *The Logical Structure of Physics. Studies in the Philosophy of Science. Proceedings of Boston Colloquia* 1961/2. Dordrecht, 1963.

WEIZSÄCKER, C.F. von, *The World View of Physics.* Routledge and Kegan Paul, London, 1952.

WHITTAKER, E.T. *Chance, Freedom and Necessity. Proc. Phys. Soc.* 55, *459, 1943.*

WINDELBAND, W. *Die Lehren vom Zufall.* F. Henschel, Berlin, 1870.

WOLF, A. *Spinoza's Short Treatise on God, Man and His Well-being.* Adam & Charles Beach, London, 1910.